VIETNAM STUDIES

COMMUNICATIONS-
ELECTRONICS
1962-1970

by

Major General Thomas Matthew Rienzi

DEPARTMENT OF THE ARMY
WASHINGTON, D.C., 1972

Library of Congress Catalog Card Number: 71–184863
First Printing

For sale by the Superintendent of Documents, U.S. Government Printing Office
Washington, D.C. 20402 - Price $1 (paper cover)
Stock Number 0820-0425

Foreword

The United States Army has met an unusually complex challenge in Southeast Asia. In conjunction with the other services, the Army has fought in support of a national policy of assisting an emerging nation to develop governmental processes of its own choosing, free of outside coercion. In addition to the usual problems of waging armed conflict, the assignment in Southeast Asia has required superimposing the immensely sophisticated tasks of a modern army upon an underdeveloped environment and adapting them to demands covering a wide spectrum. These involved helping to fulfill the basic needs of an agrarian population, dealing with the frustrations of antiguerrilla operations, and conducting conventional campaigns against well-trained and determined regular units.

As this assignment nears an end, the U.S. Army must prepare for other challenges that may lie ahead. While cognizant that history never repeats itself exactly and that no army ever profited from trying to meet a new challenge in terms of the old one, the Army nevertheless stands to benefit immensely from a study of its experience, its shortcomings no less than its achievements.

Aware that some years must elapse before the official histories will provide a detailed and objective analysis of the experience in Southeast Asia, we have sought a forum whereby some of the more salient aspects of that experience can be made available now. At the request of the Chief of Staff, a representative group of senior officers who served in important posts in Vietnam and who still carry a heavy burden of day-to-day responsibilities has prepared a series of monographs. These studies should be of great value in helping the Army develop future operational concepts while at the same time contributing to the historical record and providing the American public with an interim report on the performance of men and officers who have responded, as others have through our history, to exacting and trying demands.

All monographs in the series are based primarily on official records, with additional material from published and unpublished secondary works, from debriefing reports and interviews with key participants, and from the personal experience of the author. To facilitate security clearance, annotation and detailed bibliography have been omitted from the published version; a fully documented account with bibliography is filed with the Office of the Chief of Military History.

The qualifications of Major General Thomas Matthew Rienzi to write *Communications-Electronics* are considerable. From 1962 to 1964 he served as Signal Officer, XVIII Airborne Corps; from 1964 to 1966 as Executive Officer to the Department of the Army's Assistant Chief of Staff for Communications-Electronics and as Program Manager for Combat Surveillance Target Acquisition and Night Vision Equipment; and from 1966 to 1968 as Commanding General and Commandant of the U.S. Army Signal Center and School at Fort Monmouth, New Jersey. In all these positions he exercised a strong influence on communications-electronics personnel, organization, and equipment bound for the combat zone. In September 1968 he became the Deputy Commanding General and, in February 1969, the Commanding General of the 1st Signal Brigade in Vietnam, a larger than division size command. For twenty-one months, General Rienzi was centrally involved in the communications-electronics aspect of the U.S. effort in Southeast Asia. In June 1970 he assumed command of the Strategic Communications Command, Pacific, at Schofield Barracks, Hawaii, and serves concurrently as Deputy Chief of Staff, Communications-Electronics, U.S. Army Pacific, at Fort Shafter, Hawaii.

Washington, D.C.
15 October 1971

VERNE L. BOWERS
Major General, USA
The Adjutant General

Preface

There is an old Army maxim: "The communicators are the first ones in, and the last ones out." The 39th Signal Battalion was the first regular U.S. Army ground unit to enter Vietnam, but from this modest beginning there followed a steady buildup of Signal troops to match the initially slow but later accelerated growth of U.S. Army forces in Vietnam. By the end of 1968, the controlling Signal headquarters in Southeast Asia, the 1st Signal Brigade of the U.S. Army Strategic Communications Command, comprised six Signal groups, twenty-two Signal battalions, and a total strength of over 23,000 men—by far the largest Signal organization ever deployed to a combat theater by the United States Army. This unit of larger than division size, when coupled with the field forces Signal organizations, composed a formidable command-control force.

This study attempts to record some of the most important experiences, problems, and achievements in the field of communications-electronics during the years 1962 to 1970. It lays no claim to the definity of history.

I hope that it will show the influences that were at work and lessons learned. While I accept full responsibility for the conclusions reached, it would be misleading to pretend that I have not been influenced by my gifted predecessors, my successor, and many contemporaries, along with a tremendously outstanding group of commanders who needed enormous electronic power to do their job.

As the tempo of operations in Southeast Asia continues to diminish, the Army can look back with pride—with new wisdom— on the accomplishments, under very trying conditions, of its communicators in the Republic of Vietnam and throughout all of Southeast Asia. And a good candidate for the last Army unit to be extracted could well be a Signal battalion composed of aggressively and dynamically great American soldiers who made it all possible.

Washington, D.C.   THOMAS MATTHEW RIENZI
15 October 1971   Major General, U.S. Army

Contents

PART ONE

The Lean Years and Early Buildup, 1962–1965

PART TWO
The Buildup Climaxes, 1966–1967

Charts

Maps

Illustrations

Illustrations are from Department of Defense files except for the cartoon on page 130 by Vernon E. Grant, which appeared in Pacific *Stars and Stripes*; the photograph on page 42 of a painting by Specialist Chester Satkamp; and the photograph on page 162 of a water color by Specialist Eric K. Chandler.

PART ONE

THE LEAN YEARS AND EARLY
BUILDUP, 1962 - 1965

CHAPTER I

Background and Beginnings of Communications, 1962 - 1964

In 1962 U.S. Army Signalmen in South Vietnam began operating tropospheric scatter radio relay sets capable of providing numerous voice communications channels over extended ranges—the first use of that type of advanced equipment in a combat environment. By 1964, seven years after the Soviet Union had launched the world's first orbiting satellite, U.S. Army Signalmen were operating a new satellite ground station which provided communications service between Saigon and Hawaii through a single communications satellite thousands of miles aloft—the first use of satellite communications in combat. And by 1968 U.S. Signalmen in South Vietnam had begun to operate fully automatic digital message and data switches, another first in a combat zone. These events give some indication of the growth of Army communications during the Vietnam conflict. Any account of communications in Vietnam must include the increasing sophistication in equipment used to meet ever-growing communications needs in support of a multination effort directed toward the dual roles of nation-building and combat. Such an account must also tell the story of the dedicated, highly skilled soldiers who fought the enemy and maintained and operated that equipment in a hot, humid, underdeveloped land thousands of miles from their homes.

The Vietnam Environment

The Republic of Vietnam, located on the eastern portion of the Southeast Asia mainland, lies entirely within the tropics. (*Map 1*) The terrain is varied, with the large Mekong River Delta in the south, and alternating mountainous and highland areas in the north edging a narrow coastal plain along the South China Sea. Politically, the Republic of Vietnam is divided into forty-four provinces, which are equivalent to the fifty states of the United States. In turn, each province is made up of districts, comparable to U.S. counties.

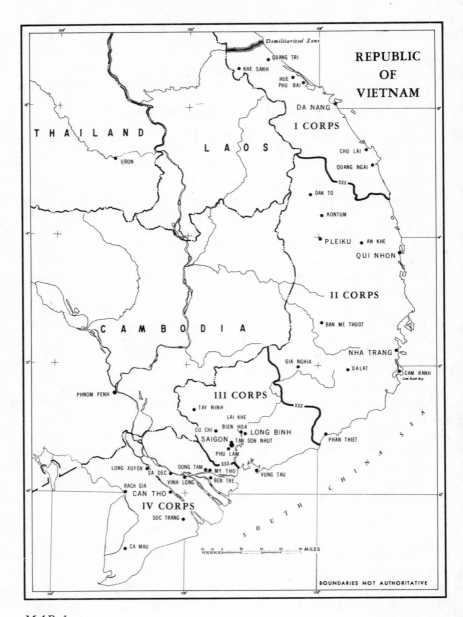

MAP 1

The weather has annual variations, from a wet, humid monsoon season to a dry season with practically no precipitation. The terrain and tropical climate have had significant effect on the U.S. Army's combat communications operations in Vietnam. In the Mekong Delta, for example, it was difficult to locate terrain suitable for the placement of communications facilities since most of the area is paddy land, which is partially submerged by the Mekong River during the rainy season, and those areas that are a few feet above water level are densely inhabited. Because of the flat terrain in the delta, tall towers reaching up to 200 feet or more were required to raise antennas to a communicable height. The muddy, silty delta lands provided a poor base for such construction. In the sparsely populated highlands and mountains, sites that afforded both feasible communications paths and reasonable access were rare. Some sites that were selected required extensive preparation, and installations were difficult to build, supply, and defend. As communications equipment became more and more sophisticated, the effects of humidity, dust, and mud were harder to overcome.

During 1959 insurgents in South Vietnam backed by the North Vietnamese were increasing their campaign of violence and subversion in an effort to obtain political control over all Vietnam. In 1960 the Communist Party of North Vietnam decided that South Vietnam was to be "liberated" and unified with the north. Subsequently, Hanoi organized a National Liberation Front and claimed that it was made up of "several political parties" in South Vietnam, with a People's Revolutionary Party identified as the leader. By 1961 the South Vietnamese Communists, termed Viet Cong or VC, were conducting, in addition to their terrorist campaign, military operations of multibattalion size in South Vietnam. The South Vietnamese Government, although it had been receiving U.S. civil and military assistance since 1954, could not cope with the worsening situation.

In late 1961, therefore, South Vietnam urgently appealed for immediate and extensive help from the United States. The U.S. Government decided to expand its assistance to South Vietnam and increased the number of U.S. military advisers from 700 to more than 3,400. Tactical aircraft and Army helicopter units were sent to Vietnam to support and train the South Vietnamese. To keep pace with the growing U.S. commitment, communications in South Vietnam required tremendous expansion.

In February 1962 the United States Military Assistance Command, Vietnam, a U.S. joint headquarters, was established to control the expanding U.S. effort and was made responsible for all U.S. military policy, operations, and assistance in South Vietnam. By that time there were over 3,000 U.S. troops in the country, advising and supporting the South Vietnamese regular military and paramilitary forces.

Communications Background and Initial Buildup

As early as 1951, U.S. Army Signal troops were providing a small U.S. advisory group in Vietnam with communications that linked into the Army's worldwide network. By the time the U.S. Military Assistance Command, Vietnam, was established, high-frequency radio circuits operated by the Strategic Army Communications station in Vietnam were providing communications from Saigon to San Miguel in the Philippines, to Fort Buckner—a large Army logistics base in Okinawa—and to Bang Pla near Bangkok in Thailand. These radio links provided a few telephone and message circuits. In addition to its high-frequency radios, the station operated an overseas telephone switchboard and the manual message relay in Saigon. At this time messages were relayed manually at a teletypewriter relay station by taking an incoming message off the receiving equipment in the form of punched tape and inserting the same tape at the appropriate send positions to transmit the message on to its destination.

The advisers, scattered up and down the more than 500-mile-long country, had to rely meanwhile on the low-capacity Vietnamese military communications networks and on a high-frequency radio network they operated themselves to pass messages and furnish telephone service. The Vietnamese commercial system was of little use since it consisted primarily of a few high-frequency radio links using old French equipment. The U.S. Agency for International Development, however, was planning the construction of a major long-lines microwave system to connect Saigon with commercial grade service throughout the country and to include local cable distribution systems.

As the U.S. effort expanded in Vietnam, the very limited communications available could not support the U.S. helicopter units, tactical aircraft, and additional advisers being deployed throughout the land. During 1961 and 1962 the joint staff of the Commander in Chief, Pacific, pushed to modernize the communications facilities in the Republic of Vietnam with two objectives: first, to create a communications system to meet the defense needs of the South Vietnamese in their counterinsurgency operations, and, second, to build it in such a way that it could be expanded to furnish the minimum needs in support of U.S. forces.

Modern radio facilities were supplied through the U.S. Military Assistance Program to improve the South Vietnamese Army's communications system. These radios provided voice and message circuits from Saigon to the outer-province cities of Da Nang, Qui Nhon, Nha Trang, Pleiku, Ban Me Thuot, and Can Tho, and sup-

U.S. Army Signalman and Vietnamese Installing a Hamlet Radio System

plemented the existing Vietnamese military high-frequency voice and morse code systems. The South Vietnamese Navy received similar radio equipment. A limited tactical air-control system which employed the integrated communications-electronics assets of the U.S. Air Force and the Republic of Vietnam was put into operation. The U.S. Military Assistance Program also supplied radio equipment to connect South Vietnamese hamlets and villages with their district headquarters, to link the district headquarters with patrols and Civil Guard posts within the district, and to connect the districts with their higher province headquarters. Province and district headquarters were also linked into the military communications networks by radio.

Long-Lines Systems: Back Porch

The increased tempo of counterinsurgency operations in Vietnam and the buildup of U.S. assistance to the Vietnamese had created an urgent requirement for a modern, reliable, large-capacity communications system that could provide high quality telephone

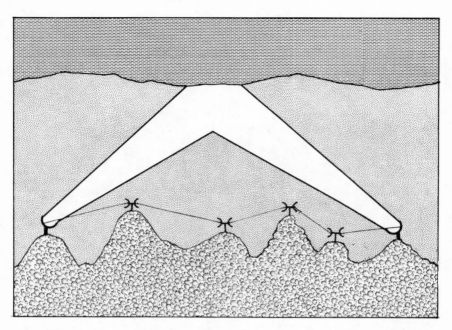

TROPOSPHERIC SCATTER AND LINE-OF-SIGHT COMMUNICATIONS

and message circuits between key locations in Vietnam. In early January 1962 Secretary of Defense Robert S. McNamara approved the establishment of a "backbone" communications system to satisfy this need. The system, code-named BACK PORCH, as conceived by planners in Washington and at the headquarters of the Commander in Chief, Pacific, would utilize tropospheric scatter radio trunks capable of providing numerous circuits between locations more than 200 miles apart. These tropospheric scatter trunks would be advantageous since, unlike conventional microwave, which needs a line of sight between sets, they would pass over the vast distances of underpopulated, enemy-infested terrain to connect the major operations and population centers in the Republic of Vietnam north of Saigon. Line-of-sight microwave relay links are limited to much shorter distances, averaging about twenty to thirty miles. From Saigon south to the delta region, long-lines service would be provided by a commercial microwave system, called SOUTHERN TOLL, funded by the U.S. Agency for International Development.

The U.S. Air Force was charged with responsibility for funding and building the BACK PORCH system; the Army would operate the system after its completion. A U.S. Army Signal support battalion, suitably structured for its special mission, was approved for deploy-

BILLBOARD ANTENNAS OF THE BACK PORCH SYSTEM AT PHU LAM IN 1962. *On top of the 60-foot tropospheric scatter antennas are the smaller antennas for mobile combat equipment that provided the "tails," or extensions.*

ment to Vietnam to operate the BACK PORCH system. It would also operate shorter range "tails," or extensions, serving scattered users, and provide service such as telephone and message communications for the U.S. forces supporting the Vietnamese. In addition, the battalion would give communications support and training to South Vietnamese armed forces.

In January 1962 the U.S. Air Force awarded a contract to furnish and install BACK PORCH. The system would consist of vans containing tropospheric scatter terminals capable of transmitting and receiving up to seventy-two voice channels simultaneously. The links of the system would extend from the Army's Saigon station at Phu Lam to Nha Trang; from Nha Trang to Qui Nhon; from Qui Nhon to Da Nang in the north; from Nha Trang to Pleiku in the Central Highlands; and west from Pleiku to a terminal in Ubon, Thailand. (*See Map 2.*)

Although these large tropospheric scatter terminals, each of which was mounted in three large semitrailers, were designed for transportable operation, their 30-foot mobile antennas could not be used because of the relatively great path lengths. More effective and permanent were the 60-foot antennas, set in concrete and resembling billboards, that were constructed instead. The system began service in September 1962 when the BACK PORCH link between Saigon and Nha Trang was activated. At the same time the U.S. Army's 39th Signal Battalion, headquartered at Tan Son Nhut, assumed responsibility for the operation of the system even though it had not been fully tested and accepted.

The 39th Signal Battalion

The 39th Signal Battalion commanded by Lieutenant Colonel Lotus B. Blackwell began to reach Vietnam in February 1962, and by midsummer the entire battalion had arrived. It had an authorized strength of over 1,000 men, consisting of a headquarters detachment and three numbered companies. The mission of the battalion was to operate and maintain the BACK PORCH system; the extensions, or tails, to the backbone system, using mobile teams and equipment; all telephone switchboard exchanges; and communications message centers in the country at that time. The 39th Signal Battalion was also responsible for telephone directory and information service; photographic service, including film and equipment exchange; motor and air courier message service; cryptographic distribution service and maintenance support for all U.S. Army and South Vietnamese units in Vietnam; signal maintenance support; and operation of the U.S. Army Signal Supply Point. The battalion was assigned to the U.S. Army Support Group, Vietnam, which, as the Army component command in Vietnam, came under the operational control of Lieutenant General Paul D. Harkins, the senior commander in Vietnam.

As the elements of the battalion arrived, they were immediately committed, installing and operating communications services for all U.S. forces in Vietnam. The 232d Signal Company was deployed in the Saigon and Mekong Delta areas to provide communications support to all the forces located there. That support included operation of manual telephone exchanges, message communications centers, high-frequency radio teletype and voice terminals, and tails of the backbone system. The 178th Signal Company, working out of Da Nang in the north, provided similar area communications support in the I and II Corps Tactical Zones located in the northern part of South Vietnam.

The 362d Signal Company, which was organized to operate the long-lines tropospheric scatter system, established its headquarters at Nha Trang in central Vietnam and immediately began deployment of its highly mobile tropospheric scatter terminals, of which

SIGNALMEN OPERATING MOBILE MANUAL SWITCHBOARD IN 1962

six were sent to Thailand. These six terminals were put into operation in January 1963 by the 362d Signal Company to furnish long-lines support to the Joint U.S. Military Advisory Group, Thailand; they were transferred to the 207th Signal Company in Thailand during December 1963. Ten of the remaining fourteen terminals were put into operation in Vietnam supplying tails from the BACK PORCH system between Da Nang and Hue, Da Nang and Quang Ngai, Pleiku and Ban Me Thuot, Saigon and Soc Trang, and Saigon and Can Tho. The Can Tho terminal was moved to Vinh Long in mid-1963. Regarding these early efforts, a brief history of the 39th Signal Battalion states: "Hardships were shared by all, often in insecure areas with . . . Viet Cong harassment. Speed was [the] order of the day and despite [rather poor] conditions, the men of the 39th, throughout the Republic of Vietnam, had begun the installation of the system."

The 39th Signal Battalion, meanwhile, was assuming more tasks. In May 1962 the battalion was charged with operating and maintaining the U.S. advisers' voice radio net. Later in December 1962 it assumed operational responsibility for the countrywide

INSTALLING INFLATABLE ANTENNA FOR A MOBILE RADIO TROPOSPHERIC SCATTER TERMINAL

U.S. advisory Operations and Intelligence Radio Net down to elements located at South Vietnamese division level. The battalion received an augmentation of over 200 soldiers from the Military Assistance Advisory Group, Vietnam, to operate this network. In order to supervise the battalion's widespread operations, located at thirty-two sites throughout South Vietnam, a System Control was established. The System Control staff also planned and engineered proposed systems.

Control and Direction Over Communications

Early in 1962 the staff of the Commander in Chief, Pacific, believing that the buildup in Vietnam required centralized control and management of long-distance communications into, out of, and within the Republic of Vietnam, recommended to the Joint Chiefs of Staff in Washington that the responsibility for the operation of the Army's worldwide communications "gateway" station in Saigon at Phu Lam be transferred from the control of the Military Assistance Advisory Group, Vietnam, back to Department of the Army and in turn to United States Army, Pacific. As it later developed, this concept required that the station continue to provide message communications support to the advisers in Vietnam and that it be attached to the 39th Signal Battalion. As a result, in September 1962 the station, consisting of 134 officers and men, was assigned to U.S. Army Support Group, Vietnam, and in addition was attached to the 39th Signal Battalion for operational control.

The station had previously become part of the worldwide Defense Communications System after the establishment of the Defense Communications Agency on 12 May 1960. In 1962 the mid-range plan of the Defense Communications Agency assigned responsibility for the Defense Communications System in Vietnam to the U.S. Army. Yet technical control and direction of this station became increasingly subject over the years to the Defense Communications Agency.

The over-all control and direction of communications in Vietnam was vested in the U.S. joint communications-electronics staff in Saigon. Direction was provided to the 39th Signal Battalion from that staff office through the Army component Signal Officer, Headquarters, U.S. Army Support Group, Vietnam. The commanding officer of the 39th Signal Battalion had dual responsibilities during this period and was referred to as being "dual-hatted." He was both battalion commander and the U.S. Army's Vietnam signal staff officer.

Improvements, Problems, and Plans to Mid-1964

During 1963 and early 1964 U.S. Army Signalmen continued to operate and improve the communications system installed in 1962 and early 1963. An additional mobile tropospheric scatter link was installed, connecting Ban Me Thuot in the Central Highlands to the small town of Gia Nghia in west central Vietnam near the famous Duc Lap Special Forces Camp. By mid-1964 a similar link was established between Gia Nghia and Saigon. Thus twenty-four channels of communications, passing over these new links and the one previously established between Ban Me Thuot and Pleiku, were available from Saigon to Pleiku in the Central Highlands. This three-link system became known as CROSSBOW. (*Map 2*)

A major improvement in the capability to relay messages into and out of the Department of Defense's worldwide network was made in January 1964 upon activation of a 50-line message relay facility operated by Strategic Army Communications Station, Viet-

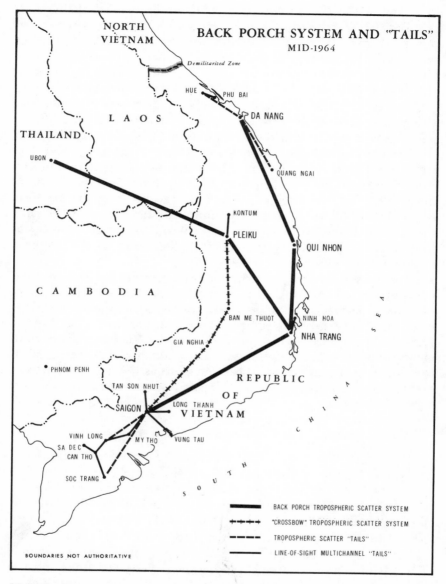

MAP. 2

nam, personnel at Phu Lam. Message traffic handled by the station steadily increased during the 1962–1963 buildup. In January 1962 the station processed over 35,000 messages. The total increased to over 117,000 in October 1963 and to more than 185,000 a month by mid-1964. Furthermore, the first circuit capable of passing low-speed data traffic was activated over the radio links of the Strategic Army Communications Station, Vietnam, connecting Saigon and the large Army logistical base in Okinawa.

The station also activated modern high-powered high-frequency transmitter equipment at Phu Lam and receiver equipment at Ba Queo, both on the outskirts of Saigon, to replace older equipment which had provided radio trunks into the worldwide Defense Communications System. These improvements were not made without difficulty. For example, when the transmitters were installed in a new building at Phu Lam, their weight caused the floor to sink into the marshy earthfill. To cope with water seepage the building had to be expanded and modified. The new facilities improved the quality of communications consisting, by early 1963, of 16 message and 3 voice channels operating on the high-frequency radio trunk to Okinawa, 16 message and 3 voice channels to the Philippines, and 12 message and 3 voice channels to Thailand.

A new Saigon overseas switchboard was installed at Phu Lam to improve long-distance telephone service. This manual switchboard had positions for four operators. However, even with this improvement, there were difficulties in placing overseas calls because of the limited reliability of high-frequency radio, particularly when operated in Southeast Asia. According to a history of the Phu Lam Signal Battalion, "The switchboard logs consistently included entries such as 'out,' 'out to fair,' 'poor to fair,' and 'out all day.' " By the end of October 1963 the switchboard was averaging thirty-three overseas calls a day, while later, at its peak in 1968–1970, over 1,500 calls were processed each day.

The Commander in Chief, Pacific, recognizing the limitations of these radio systems, had proposed as early as June 1961 a wideband system to furnish high quality communications throughout the Western Pacific defense line. The system would interconnect Korea, Japan, Okinawa, Taiwan, the Philippines, South Vietnam, and Thailand. It would also link up with commercial undersea cables to provide circuits from Hawaii to Japan and the Philippines. The part of the system between the Philippines and Vietnam would consist of a 55-mile microwave system between Clark Air Force Base and San Miguel in the Philippines; an 800-mile submarine cable between San Miguel and Nha Trang in South Vietnam; and a tropospheric scatter radio link connecting Nha Trang with Saigon. The Air Force, which was responsible for establishing the system, awarded the contract for construction in November 1963. This system, called WET WASH, which was not completed until

January 1965, had a capacity of sixty voice channels from Southeast Asia to the Philippines. The Air Force was then charged with operating the system from the Philippines to Nha Trang; the Army was responsible for operation of the tropospheric scatter link between Nha Trang and Saigon.

Since communications with Thailand also needed improvement, a 24-channel tropospheric scatter system was proposed early in the 1960s to be installed between Saigon and Bangkok. The Army was made responsible for this 450-mile single-hop system, with Philco-Ford Corporation as the construction contractor. When activated in mid-1963, the system did not perform well because the distance proved too great for operation over the path between the original site locations. It was re-engineered with terminals located at a site called VC Hill, southeast of Saigon near Vung Tau, in Vietnam, and a camp at Green Hill, north of Bangkok, in Thailand. This revamped system, scheduled for completion by September 1965, the world's longest single-hop tropospheric scatter system at the time, became operational in December 1965.

For a while in the early 1960s optimism ran high at General Paul D. Harkins' joint headquarters, in anticipation of an early end to hostilities. For example, a telecommunications plan of June 1963 called for phasing out the Army's 39th Signal Battalion. This plan, which was modified by the staff of the Commander in Chief, Pacific, Admiral Harry D. Felt, and later approved by the Joint Chiefs of Staff, envisaged that the communications operated by the Army would be turned over to the Republic of Vietnam. By the end of 1963 the 39th Signal Battalion was training South Vietnamese troops to operate its mobile radio relay equipment. Plans which had assumed that the Viet Cong could be eliminated by the end of 1964 provided the basis for communications efforts up to mid-1964. But they were precluded by events which drastically changed the requirements for communications in Southeast Asia.

CHAPTER II

Military Intensifies Communications Activities, 1964–1965

Before the 39th Signal Battalion could make much progress toward training Vietnamese communications personnel, optimistic plans looking toward an early military solution of the war were wrecked by current events. In November 1963, South Vietnam's first president, Ngo Dinh Diem, was assassinated and his government overthrown. There followed a series of rapidly changing governments, producing a state of disorganization that seriously weakened the South Vietnamese efforts against the Viet Cong. Meanwhile, in early 1964, Hanoi decided to infiltrate North Vietnamese Regular Army troops into South Vietnam to defeat the disorganized and confused South Vietnamese. Hanoi also started to equip the Viet Cong with modern automatic weapons.

The Tonkin Gulf incidents of early August 1964 marked the first direct engagements between North Vietnamese and U.S. forces and, according to General William C. Westmoreland, "represented a crucial psychological turning point in the course of the Vietnam War." By December 1964 the North Vietnamese had infiltrated no less than 12,000 troops, including a North Vietnamese Army regiment, into South Vietnam. At the same time a Viet Cong division had been organized and was engaged in combat operations. In order to bolster the faltering South Vietnamese forces, the United States deployed additional advisers and support units. The Republic of South Vietnam forces were increased by 117,000 men during 1964, attaining a strength of over 514,000. Their effectiveness, however, decreased markedly. Through the last half of that year U.S. troop strength increased rapidly. The number was approximately 16,000 in June of 1964 when General Westmoreland assumed the responsibilities of Commander, United States Military Assistance Command, Vietnam. By the year's end, U.S. troops in Vietnam numbered about 23,000.

Satellite Communications Come to Vietnam

The inadequacy and unreliability of the meager radio circuits linking Vietnam with Hawaii and Washington became painfully evident during the 1964 Gulf of Tonkin incidents. In the first week of August the engagement of U.S. Navy vessels by North Vietnamese torpedo boats resulted in a flurry of telephone calls and messages between Saigon and Washington. The long-haul high-frequency radio circuits, hampered by severe sunspot activity and occasional transmitter failure in Saigon, were simply not capable of carrying the load. The WET WASH cable project, which would subsequently bring highly reliable services into Southeast Asia, was not yet complete.

An experimental satellite ground terminal, with an operating team under Warrant Officer Jack H. Inman, was rushed to Vietnam to bolster communications capabilities. The terminal, which provided one telephone and one teletype circuit to Hawaii, became operational in late August 1964. Signals were relayed from Saigon to Hawaii through a communications satellite launched into a stationary orbit some 22,000 statute miles above the Pacific Ocean. This experimental synchronous communications satellite system, dubbed SYNCOM, was the first use of satellite communications in a combat zone. The satellite ground terminal in Vietnam, which was operated by the U.S. Army's Strategic Communications Command, provided the earliest reliable communications of high quality into and out of Vietnam.

The SYNCOM satellite communications service was improved in October 1964 with a newer terminal that provided one telephone and sixteen message circuits. These "space age" communications means immediately proved their worth. The Command History, 1964, of the United States Military Assistance Command, Vietnam, states: "Since October the . . . [satellite terminal] has handled a remarkable volume of operational traffic." And further: "It appears that satellite communications are here to stay and will increase MACV [Military Assistance Command, Vietnam] capability in the future."

System Problems, Further Plans, and Control Matters

Communications deficiencies within Vietnam became more apparent as the hard-pressed signalmen struggled to provide the communications service required by the new buildup. As early as mid-1963 it was recognized that the single 72-channel tropospheric scatter link between Saigon and Nha Trang did not have sufficient

FIRST SATELLITE TERMINAL, BA QUEO, NEAR SAIGON. *This station linked Vietnam with Hawaii in first use of satellite communications in a combat zone.*

capacity to pass the required traffic from Nha Trang, where two other 72-channel systems from Pleiku and Qui Nhon converged for interconnections to the south. The BACK PORCH sites had been chosen as a compromise between the ease of maintaining site protection and securing the radio propagation characteristics required for operation. As a result some links performed poorly, the poorest link being the saturated one between Saigon and Nha Trang.

Another shortcoming of the long-lines systems which steadily became more apparent was the lack of adequate facilities to control, test, and interconnect circuits, that is, the lack of technical control facilities at the channel breakout or switch locations such as Nha Trang, Pleiku, and Qui Nhon. Colonel Thomas W. Riley, Jr., who was the U.S. Army, Vietnam, Signal Officer in 1965, later recalled: "It was ironical that such big costly refined . . . links as . . . provided at Pleiku—involving a . . . [multimillion dollar] installation connecting Nha Trang to the east with . . . [Ubon, Thailand] to the west—came together at Pleiku in a shed." As more and more tails using mobile equipment were installed, branching off the BACK PORCH commercial grade system, various technical difficulties were encountered. Among these were differences in the voice channel electrical current levels where the circuits interconnected, and differences in the signaling frequencies that are employed to ring the telephone of the distant person who is being called. Without adequate technical control facilities at the circuit interconnecting points it was difficult to "match" electrically the incompatible equipment. Also, where circuits had to be rerouted or activated in support of fast-moving operations, the inadequate technical control facilities could not respond rapidly. Furthermore, the mobile equipment was not designed to operate at the low noise levels associated with more sophisticated high quality "commercial" grade systems. These differences of channel levels, system noise levels, and ringing frequencies, and the lack of adequate technical control facilities all made for a system of degraded quality. Since high-speed data can pass only over high quality communications systems, it was becoming increasingly important to provide noiseless, error-free circuits so that data traffic could be accurately received at the distant end.

As a result of both these technical problems and the requirements generated by the buildup, the Commander in Chief, Pacific, by October 1964 had validated requirements to the Joint Chiefs of Staff for additional communications service. These requirements became known as Phase I of the Integrated Wideband Communications System. A wideband communications system as described in the Military Assistance Command Vietnam History of 1965 is "a communications system which provides numerous channels of communication on a highly reliable basis; included are multichannel telephone cable, troposcatter, and multi-channel line of sight radio systems such as microwave."

This communications project would include the establishment of a BACK PORCH type of system in Thailand. The Vietnam portion as visualized by the planners would provide support for up to 40,000 U.S. troops by upgrading the existing fixed tropospheric scatter communications; by improving service in the Saigon area; by establishing an additional link north to bypass the system between Saigon and Nha Trang, extending additional channels north from the Saigon area and from the Da Nang area still further north to Phu Bai; and by installing adequate technical control facilities throughout the system.

By December 1964 the Defense Communications Agency had prepared a plan and forwarded it through the Joint Chiefs of Staff to the Secretary of Defense for approval. According to this plan the wideband system would become a part of the Defense Communications System under a Defense Communications Agency control center located in Saigon. The authority to validate customer requirements for the use of circuits was vested with the communications-electronics staffs of the U.S. military assistance commands in Vietnam and Thailand.

The Department of Defense, while the plan was being studied, decided to use permanent, fixed installations rather than large transportable shelters for the system. This decision would require construction of buildings and other facilities in Southeast Asia to house the equipment. The decision was made on the basis that time was the critical factor—the system was needed right then—and the contractors were promising that the system could be operational one year after contract award if commercial equipment and prefabricated buildings were used. The use of "transportables," that is, commercial equipment installed in large vans similar to the equipment used on BACK PORCH, was considered; it was estimated, however, that transportables would require more time to manufacture and put into operation than a fixed system and that they would be more costly.

The plan called for the system to be operational by 1 December 1965, an early date that proved altogether too optimistic. For example, the plan was not approved for contracting action until the Department of Defense approved it as a "Telecommunications Program Objective" in August 1965. The U.S. Army, which was designated as the contracting agency, awarded the contract for the Vietnam portion of the system to Page Communications Engineers, Inc., in September 1965. The system would be operated by the U.S. Army Strategic Communications Command, which was originally activated on 1 April 1962 by combining the U.S. Army Signal Engineering Agency and the U.S. Army Communications Agency. This was in line with its mission as the Army's single operator of those portions of the worldwide Defense Communications System assigned as an Army responsibility.

Organizational and control arrangements changed during this period. The U.S. Army Support Group, Vietnam, was redesignated as the U.S. Army Support Command, Vietnam, in March 1964, when the dual-hat status of the Army component command signal officer also changed. Previously, he had served both as the Army Support Group Signal Officer and as the Commanding Officer, 39th Signal Battalion. But following the reorganization, the positions were allocated separately; according to personnel lists of

March 1964, Lieutenant Colonel Earl R. Velie became Signal Officer of the Army Support Command and Major Leo T. White became Commanding Officer, 39th Signal Battalion.

Also in 1964 the command and control arrangements for the big Strategic Army Communications Station, Vietnam, were affected by the creation and expansion of the U.S. Army Strategic Communications Command and its Pacific subcommand headquartered in Hawaii. In November 1964 the station was redesignated Strategic Communications Facility, Vietnam, and at about the same time control of the facility passed from U.S. Army Support Command, Vietnam, to U.S. Army Strategic Communications Command, Pacific. These changes in 1964 marked the beginning of a division of control over Army communications in Vietnam between the Army Strategic Communications Command and the Army component command signal troops.

By the spring of 1965 the combat situation had deteriorated further. The casualties of the South Vietnamese Army were mounting to the point that the equivalent of almost one infantry battalion a week was being lost. In March the United States sent Army airborne and Marine combat troops to defend U.S. air bases in Vietnam against enemy attack. In order to support these forces, it was necessary to deploy a logistical command and other combat support troops. An additional signal unit, the 41st Signal Battalion, and Headquarters, 2d Signal Group, were alerted for movement to Vietnam.

By mid-1965 it had been decided to commit substantial numbers of U.S. fighting troops along with other combat support organizations. The emphasis was on the introduction of infantry, armor, and artillery elements. As General Westmoreland relates in his report on the war in Vietnam: "There were inadequate ports and airfields, no logistic organization, and no supply, transportation, or maintenance troops. None the less, in the face of the grave tactical situation, I decided to accept combat troops as rapidly as they could be made available and to improvise their logistic support." By the end of 1965 U.S. strength in Vietnam stood at 184,000 men.

The 2d Signal Group Arrives

The first of the additional Signal Corps troops to reach Vietnam was the advance party of Headquarters, 2d Signal Group, commanded by Colonel James J. Moran, which arrived from Fort Bragg, North Carolina, in May 1965. Five companies of the 41st

Signal Battalion, commanded by Lieutenant Colonel James G. Pelland, arrived in late June, and the rest of the battalion was in Vietnam by 14 July 1965. A separate company, the 593d Signal Company, arrived in Saigon on 13 July 1965. By mid-July the 2d Signal Group had reached an authorized strength of about 2,900 officers and men.

The 2d Signal Group, upon its arrival, assumed command of the 39th Signal Battalion, taking over in fact all the missions previously assigned that battalion, such as the tasks of providing signal maintenance support and operation of the signal supply system in Vietnam. Later, these supply and maintenance missions were turned over to the 1st Logistical Command. Upon acquiring its second signal unit, the 41st Signal Battalion, in mid-1965, the 2d Signal Group made it responsible for all area communications in the northern half of the Republic of Vietnam in the I and II Corps Tactical Zones, while assigning responsibility to the 39th Signal Battalion for the southern half of Vietnam in the III and IV Corps Tactical Zones. The 362d Signal Company was also placed directly under the 2d Signal Group to operate the tropospheric scatter system throughout the country. The group was assigned to U.S. Army Support Command, Vietnam, and subsequently to U.S. Army, Vietnam, when the latter was established on 20 July 1965, replacing the Support Command. The U.S. Army, Vietnam, was also commanded by General Westmoreland, who served concurrently as Commander, U.S. Military Assistance Command, Vietnam.

These new Regular Army signal units immediately went to work to improve the existing communications and establish communications for new base areas. For example, by mid-July mobile equipment was provided to support the new logistical base being established at Cam Ranh Bay. A 12-voice channel radio relay link was installed to connect Cam Ranh with Nha Trang. A one-position tactical switchboard was put into operation, a mobile communications message center was installed, and high-powered radios linked Cam Ranh into radio nets in Vietnam. In just a few weeks the small switchboard at Cam Ranh had to be replaced with another mobile manual board that was much larger—a 3-position switchboard capable of serving 200 subscribers. Microwave teams with mobile equipment had arrived in Nha Trang to start installation of a 45-channel microwave link between Cam Ranh Bay and Nha Trang. By the end of October 1965 arrangements had been made to ship a fixed-plant, automatic dial telephone exchange to Cam Ranh Bay. The fixed automatic dial telephone equipment

MAN-PACKED RADIO OPERATED BY COMBAT SIGNALMAN IN 1965

required a dust-free, humidity-controlled environment for operation, hence special building construction was required.

Colonel Moran's 2d Signal Group was also busily engaged in
providing communications support to the combat troops, both to
those that were already in Vietnam and to those that were being
sent to the country. The group was alerted on 12 August 1965 to
provide communications support to the famous 173d Airborne Brigade for an important Vietnam highlands operation in the Pleiku
area. The next day the necessary equipment and Signal Corps
troops were airlifted to Pleiku, and by evening on 14 August communications got into operation, linking the 173d's operating area
into the large fixed backbone system at Pleiku.

Equipment and personnel also had to be redistributed to support arriving units. During the week of 15–21 August, twenty-four
tons of signal equipment were moved to the I and II Corps Tactical Zones by special airlift, while an additional twenty-eight tons
were awaiting movement. By early September 1965 U.S. Army,
Vietnam, had established priorities for providing communications
support throughout the country. First priority would go to the

combat units, second to combat support elements, and third to logistic and administrative elements.

Command and Control Arrangements

During this period General Westmoreland's joint headquarters was establishing and refining command control arrangements in Vietnam. The final arrangement provided that the Commander, U.S. Military Assistance Command, Vietnam, exercise tactical control over the U.S. forces through the III Marine Amphibious Force in the northern I Corps Tactical Zone, through the I Field Force in the II Corps Tactical Zone, and through the II Field Force in the III Corps Tactical Zone. Both field force headquarters were modified U.S. Army Corps headquarters. A senior U.S. adviser was responsible for controlling and co-ordinating U.S. advisory and support troop efforts in the IV Corps Tactical Zone. The Seventh Air Force controlled all U.S. Air Force units, while United States Army, Vietnam, controlled all Army support and logistical units. The I Field Force, initially designated Task Force Alpha, was activated in August 1965, II Field Force headquarters during the spring of 1966.

When Task Force Alpha was activated in August, no signal organization to support it in central Vietnam was available. Interim communications support was provided for Task Force Alpha, headquartered at Nha Trang, by the 2d Signal Group. But on 15 September 1965 the organic 54th Corps Signal Battalion of Task Force Alpha started to arrive and by 1 October began to relieve the 2d Signal Group. The final elements of the 54th closed into Vietnam in October, thus freeing the overtaxed communicators of the 2d Signal Group to work in other areas in Vietnam. Initial communications support for II Field Force at Long Binh, fifteen miles northwest of Saigon, also had to be provided by the 2d Signal Group during the spring of 1966 until the 53d Signal Battalion arrived to provide the needed support.

Additional Communications Control Elements Enter Vietnam

Changes were being made, meanwhile, in higher level communications control, direction, and operations responsibilities. In line with plans for the integrated wideband system that called for establishment of a Defense Communications Agency center in Vietnam, the Deputy Secretary of Defense approved the manning of the Defense Communications Agency, Support Center, Saigon, on 29 April 1965. The support center would provide "system control and engineering support" to both the military assistance command in Vietnam and that in Thailand. The center itself would also be subject to the authority of Defense Communications Agency, Southeast Asia Region, located at Clark Air Force Base in the Philippines. The first Support Center elements arrived in Vietnam during May 1965. In early June U.S. Military Assistance Command, Vietnam, assigned to the center additional tasks, including operational direction and restoration authority for all Defense Communications circuits in Vietnam. The Vietnam circuits included those passing over the BACK PORCH system, which would be integrated into the new wideband system as part of the worldwide Defense Communications System. This new mission also required that the Defense Communications Agency element in Vietnam supervise and restore defense circuits which passed over the mobile tails, down to and including the subscribers' instrument, controlled by the Army component signal troops under the 2d Signal Group.

In September 1965 the Defense Communications Agency, Support Center, Saigon, was redesignated Defense Communications Agency, Southeast Asia Mainland Region. As a part of the Defense Communications Agency organizational structure, the region came under the Pacific area office located in Hawaii. By the end of 1965 the strength of the Southeast Asia Mainland Region had grown from eight men to 100.

In May 1965 Department of the Army directed that those facilities and personnel which would become a part of the Defense Communications System be transferred from U.S. Army, Pacific, to the Army's Strategic Communications Command. This directive was in line with the Strategic Communications Command's mission to operate the Army's portion of the Defense Communications System. In July 1965 the command established an organization to operate the backbone system in Southeast Asia, namely, the U.S. Army Strategic Communications Command, Pacific, Southeast Asia, located in Saigon. Subordinate elements of this new organization were formed in both Vietnam and Thailand and were charged with the actual operation of the system. Elements of the command's 11th Signal Group stationed at Fort Lewis, Washington, arrived in Vietnam in June 1965 to establish the headquarters of the Strategic Communications Command in Southeast Asia. Colonel Henry Schneider was designated as commander of all the Strategic Communications Command's troops in Southeast Asia, while Lieutenant Colonel Jerry J. Enders, who arrived with the unit from Fort Lewis, was designated to command the Vietnam element. Arrangements were made for turning over the Defense Communications System facilities of the tropospheric scatter systems operated by the 2d Signal Group for BACK PORCH and WET WASH and those at Green Hill in Thailand and Saigon in Vietnam.

Not until 19 August 1965 did the 2d Signal Group turn over to the Strategic Communications Command in Vietnam the responsibility for operation of these systems, along with the transfer of 121 officers and men. These developments increased the command's problems and widened the split in Army communications operations in Vietnam between the Army's Strategic Communications Command's organizations and the area support signal units of the 2d Signal Group under the Army component headquarters, U.S. Army, Vietnam.

A like transfer occurred in Thailand. The U.S. Army's 379th Signal Battalion, which had been organized in Thailand in April 1965, assigned one officer and 71 enlisted men to the Strategic Communications Command element in Thailand in September 1965. The 379th provided mobile communications support to U.S. forces in Thailand similar to that provided by the 39th Signal Battalion in Vietnam.

The Army's Strategic Communications Facility, Vietnam, continued to remain directly under the Hawaii-based Strategic Communications Command, Pacific, headquarters until November 1965, when the station was assigned to the Strategic Communications Command element in Vietnam and was redesignated U.S. Army Strategic Communications Command Facility, Phu Lam. This vital gateway station continued to handle most of the communications passing into and out of Vietnam. The preponderance of the traffic flowed over the high quality circuits of the WET WASH undersea cable to the Philippines.

Earlier at the Phu Lam facility, on 23 March 1965, the first manual data relay center had been activated. At that time the data relay had three connected stations, Clark Air Force Base in the Philippines, Tan Son Nhut Air Base on the outskirts of Saigon, and the Army's 27th Data Processing Unit in Saigon. The station relayed 11,000 cards on its first day of operation. At the end of 1965 the station was processing approximately 400,000 cards per month from seven connected stations.

Early in 1965 the Phu Lam message relay with its twenty-five active circuits also was processing over 250,000 messages per month. By September the station began to experience extreme difficulty in handling the message traffic. The backlog of service messages became critical when at times up to 1,000 were awaiting action. Because of the deteriorating situation at Phu Lam, the only Defense Communications System message relay facility in Vietnam, an interim tape relay facility, using large transportable vans capable of terminating eighteen circuits, was deployed to Vietnam. These Strategic Communications Command contingency or emergency assets, which arrived in Nha Trang on 25 October, were operational by 3 November 1965. By the close of the year these two major message relays at Saigon and Nha Trang were processing over half a million messages per month out of and into Vietnam over circuits of the Defense Communications System.

More Mobile Radio, More Fixed Radio, and Cable

As more troops were deployed throughout the Republic of Vietnam, it became apparent that the existing BACK PORCH system and the planned Integrated Wideband Communications System could not support the critical circuit needs in Vietnam. Contingency transportable tropospheric scatter equipment was provided to Vietnam beginning in March 1965 when six Army mobile terminals arrived. These were used to establish additional circuits north from Saigon to Pleiku through a single relay point situated near the summit of the 7,000-foot mountain, Niu Lang Bian, which stood a few miles to the north of Dalat in the south central highlands. Initially installed as a 24-channel system, its capacity was increased in late summer to forty-eight voice channels when two terminals of another system were redeployed to provide the additional channelizing equipment.

Six larger tropospheric scatter terminals similar to those of the BACK PORCH system were also deployed and operational by the end of 1965. Using their transportable antennas these terminals established twenty-four voice channel links between Pleiku and Da Nang, Vung Tau and Cam Ranh Bay, and between Da Nang and Ubon, Thailand. These systems, along with other tails provided by the 2d Signal Group, had added approximately 35,000 voice channel miles to the Vietnam communications system during the last half of 1965. (*Map 3*) None of these statistics on facilities, however, included the numerous systems installed by the 2d Signal Group in direct support of combat operations.

Furthermore, the mobile systems were all stopgap measures. Additional circuits of the fixed type were required to support the expanding effort, particularly for the low priority logistical forces and their complex widespread operations. By the end of 1965, the U.S. joint headquarters in Saigon had forwarded three require-

MOBILE TROPOSPHERIC SCATTER ANTENNA ON NUI LANG BIAN NEAR DALAT *was installed and defended by U.S. Army Signalmen in late 1965.*

ments packages to the Commander in Chief, Pacific, which, as conceived by the U.S. Military Assistance Command and component communications planners, would provide the necessary long-lines support in Vietnam. The first package forwarded in October was an addition to the programmed wideband system and was later called Integrated Wideband Communications System, Phase II; it was designed to support up to 200,000 troops. The second requirements package, sent in November 1965, requested a coastal submarine cable system to supplement the integrated wideband system. The third package, forwarded to the Commander in Chief, Pacific, in December 1965, was designed to support up to 400,000 troops.

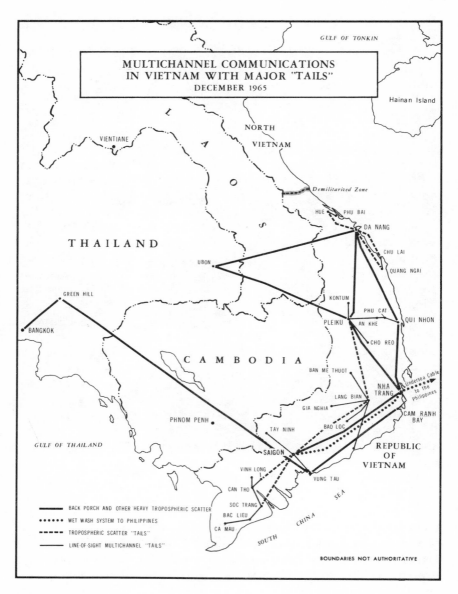

MAP 3

This final major addition to the integrated system was later called Integrated Wideband Communications System, Phase III. The system would provide commercial grade service using fixed-plant equipment and construction techniques.

More Buildup and Combat Needs

As the troop buildup continued, from late summer until the end of the year the 2d Signal Group found it more and more difficult to provide enough communications support. By July there were three U.S. Army combat brigades in Vietnam: the 173d Airborne Brigade, commanded by Brigadier General Ellis W. Williamson, had arrived in May of 1965; the other two, the 1st Brigade of the 101st Airborne Division and the 2d Brigade of the 1st Infantry Division, had arrived in July. U.S. and other Free World Military Assistance Forces began to arrive in division-size units along with all required communications support. The first complete U.S. Army division to reach Vietnam was the 1st Cavalry Division, Airmobile, which arrived in September 1965. The U.S. Army's 1st Infantry Division, whose commander was Major General Jonathan O. Seaman, the Republic of Korea Capital Division, and a Korean Marine brigade all arrived in October. By December the lead element, the 3d Brigade, of the U.S. Army's 25th Infantry Division was in Vietnam. Although the planners were allotting a U.S. Army combat area signal company and a signal support company for each division-size force, these units were not initially available. The signal troops already in Vietnam would have to improvise the needed support. Communications service into the system of Vietnam was provided by installing mobile radio relay links connected to the backbone system. Only limited telephone and message service could be made available. The divisions had to install and operate a good portion of their communications, using the organic capability of their division signal battalions, until Army signal support units arrived.

The organic 121st Signal Battalion of the U.S. 1st Infantry Division was one of those that initially had to provide all communication services to its division without the supplemental benefit of Army area type signal support. At first, the 121st was located in a staging area near Bien Hoa, but as the division spread out, so did the signal battalion. The battalion headquarters and two of its three signal companies moved to the division base camp in Di An, approximately fifteen miles northwest of Saigon. Company B, the forward communications company, deployed its three platoons with the far-flung Big Red One infantry brigades north of Di An.

From this configuration, the organic 121st Signal Battalion operated and maintained all of the communications support for the division. The signalmen installed the myriad command and control as well as administrative telephone and message circuits that tied together the five major base camps of the division. They also operated the overloaded switchboards and overworked message centers at these base camps. And because the 1st Infantry Division was engaged in active combat from the first day of its arrival, the 121st Signal Battalion supported all combat operations by running the division's command and control radio nets and providing essential combat telephone and message circuits from each infantry brigade or battalion command post back to the main base camp at Di An.

It was not until May 1966, some seven months after the 121st Signal Battalion became operational in Vietnam, that assistance arrived in the form of the 595th Signal Company. This recently arrived unit of the 2d Signal Group immediately helped relieve the pressure on the 1st Infantry Division's communicators by taking over their switchboard and multichannel radio operations at Di An. The pattern of communications support, as it rapidly evolved in the 1st Infantry Division area, would continue throughout the Vietnam War: the organic signal unit, in this case the 121st Signal Battalion, provided the command and control communications so essential to the field commander and supported the combat operations, while the supporting Army area signal unit provided the administrative or general-user communications, tying the base camps together and affording entry into the countrywide Defense Communications System.

While the 1st Cavalry Division and its organic 13th Signal Battalion, commanded by Lieutenant Colonel Tom M. Nicholson, were deploying to the An Khe area in the Vietnamese Central Highlands, midway between Pleiku and Qui Nhon, the 586th Signal Support Company arrived in Vietnam. The company was immediately attached to the 41st Signal Battalion and sent to An Khe to support the 1st Cavalry Division. This attachment proved wise because the airmobile division, newest of Army divisions along with its completely equipped but lightweight signal battalion, was about to be tested under fire in the fully developed airmobile concept. The men of the 13th Signal Battalion soon had much more on their minds than installing base camp wire systems and operating switchboards at An Khe, their base of operations.

In October 1965 the North Vietnamese concentrated three regiments of their best troops in the Central Highlands in an area between the Cambodian border and the Special Forces camp at Plei Me. On 19 October the enemy opened his campaign with an attack on the Plei Me camp, which lays twenty-five miles southwest of Pleiku. The North Vietnamese commander attacked with one

SKYTROOPERS OF 1ST CAVALRY DIVISION PREPARE TO BOARD ASSAULT HELICOPTERS FOR PLEI ME

regiment, holding the bulk of his division-size force in reserve. With the aid of concentrated tactical air strikes, the South Vietnamese Army in the area repelled the attack. On 27 October General Westmoreland directed the 1st Cavalry Division into combat, its mission to seek out and destroy the enemy force in western Pleiku Province. Thus began the month-long campaign known as the Battle of the Ia Drang Valley.

Almost immediately, thanks to the helicopter, the division commander, Major General Harry W. O. Kinnard, was able to send a division forward tactical operation center to Pleiku. And hot on its heels followed troops and equipment of the 13th Signal Battalion in heavy-lift cargo helicopters. The battalion rapidly installed a combat radio relay system from the division forward to each of the deployed brigade headquarters—a definite asset throughout the long battle. By means of the system each brigade had direct telephone and message contact with both the division forward tactical operations center and the division base at An Khe. Sole-user command and control circuits were extended from the I Field Force headquarters at Nha Trang to General Kinnard's division forward operations center at Pleiku. The U.S. Air Force liaison officer at the forward command post in Pleiku was also provided with sole-user circuits. These sole-user circuits proved invaluable during the last and most intense phases of the Ia Drang battle.

Shortly after the start of the operation to relieve the besieged Plei Me Special Forces Camp, it was found that the infantry units, the companies and battalions in contact with the enemy, were having difficulty maintaining communications with their higher headquarters. It did not take long to pinpoint the problem; the short-range, man-packed voice radios in use simply could not cope with the great distances and the fact that the jungle undergrowth of the Central Highlands absorbed electrical energy.

Fortunately the 1st Cavalry Division's 13th Signal Battalion had prepared for this very contingency while still testing the airmobile concept at Fort Benning, Georgia. The problem was solved by placing specially configured combat voice radios in the U.S. Army's Caribou aircraft and orbiting the craft and their radios above those ground units that were using the small portable sets. The result was an airborne relay that could automatically retransmit up to six combat radio nets over far greater distances than the ground range of the radios. Thus at Ia Drang the units on the ground were served by the 13th Signal Battalion's airborne relay twenty-four hours a day for the last twenty-eight days of the campaign. The optimum altitude turned out to be nine to ten thousand feet above ground, effectively extending the range of the small combat radios fifty to sixty miles, even when the radios were operating in the most dense undergrowth. However, this method of communications, while highly successful in the Ia Drang area, is very costly in manpower and equipment and raises many radio frequency interference problems.

As the enemy withdrew his assault regiment from Plei Me, it suffered severe casualties from air strikes and the pursuing air cavalry. But when the 1st Cavalry Division put a blocking force behind the withdrawing enemy, only a few miles from the Cambodian border, the North Vietnamese commander committed his remaining two regiments in an attempt to redeem his earlier failure at Plei Me by destroying a major U.S. unit—the 3d Brigade, 1st Cavalry Division, barely thirty days in Vietnam. The 3d Brigade, however, commanded by Colonel Harold G. Moore, Jr., decisively defeated each enemy regiment in turn and the combined efforts of the division literally swept the Ia Drang valley clear of North Vietnamese.

As in almost all combat action in the Vietnam War, the Ia Drang campaign was not an Army effort alone, but rather a combined air and ground effort. Usually tactical fighter aircraft of the Air Force and the Navy were used in direct support of combat operations. Here for the first time in the Vietnam conflict, the U.S.

Air Force strategic bombers, the huge B–52s, were used in general support of the ground combat commander's scheme of maneuver. Hitherto communications had not been good enough to permit the close co-ordination required to employ bombing missions when friendly troops were going to be anywhere in the vicinity. But now direct links between the field commander and his higher headquarters and the direct lines to the U.S. Air Force's Direct Air Support Center, greatly reduced the reaction time. The field commanders of the 1st Cavalry Division could now use the awesome, destructive power of B–52 air strikes as part of the normal planned air missions and for the first time this strategic weapon would be used tactically.

The classic campaign of the Ia Drang valley during the last months of 1965 proved the soundness of the airmobile concept: ground soldiers, aviators, and communicators were successfully molded into a potent, flexible, fighting force.

As U.S. Army and other combat units continued to pour into the country, adding to the communications load of the 2d Signal Group, welcome assistance arrived when the 578th Signal Construction Company landed at Cam Ranh Bay and was attached to the 41st Signal Battalion. Help also came from the 228th Signal Company, attached to the 39th Signal Battalion, which was stationed in the newly established logistical area at Long Binh near Bien Hoa. The 228th provided additional multichannel radio relay capability in the III and IV Corps Tactical Zones. But there were still not enough communications. Brigadier General John Norton, General Westmoreland's deputy commander of the U.S. Army, Vietnam, was emphatic on that score. In the late summer of 1965 he stated in a command report:

Communications continues to be a major command problem. I estimate our capability by 31 December will be 1,735 channels, which, considering customer needs, will make an average deficit of 30%. On some major axes, the deficit will be higher, such as Saigon–Nha Trang (61%), and Nha Trang–Qui Nhon (50%).

In November 1965 the 1,300-man 69th Signal Battalion (Army) commanded by Lieutenant Colonel Charles R. Meyer, arrived, along with the 580th Signal Company (Construction). The 69th Signal Battalion took over operation of all local communications support in the Saigon–Long Binh area. Besides providing area signal support for the numerous troop units, the 69th directly supported the headquarters of the U.S. Military Assistance Command, Vietnam, U.S. Army, Vietnam, and the U.S. Army's 1st Logistical Command. To assist in this massive effort, the 593d Signal

SOLDIER DIRECTS LANDING OF RESUPPLY HELICOPTER DURING IA DRANG
BATTLE

Company, which had been providing communications support in
the Saigon area, was attached. The 580th Signal Company, which
was capable of installing large fixed cable systems, was also attached.

The last signal unit to arrive during 1965 was the 518th Signal
Company, which reached Vietnam in late December. This company, capable of operating mobile tropospheric scatter and microwave equipment, relieved the 362d Signal Company of the responsibility for the operation of the mobile tropospheric scatter and
microwave systems in the III and IV Corps Tactical Zones in the
south. With these additions Colonel Moran's 2d Signal Group had
grown to a strength of nearly 6,000 by the end of the year. *(Chart 1)*

Even so, adequate communications service could not keep pace
with the growing number of "customer" requirements. At the end
of 1965 General Norton in his quarterly report continued to list
inadequate communications:

The inadequacies of some major axes of long lines communications in
USARV still remain alarmingly high: Saigon–Nha Trang 52%, and
Nha Trang–Qui Nhon 50%. Programmed installation of multichannel
equipment has proceeded as planned, and every measure available to
the command is being taken to obviate the situation.

CHART 1—SIGNAL ORGANIZATION IN VIETNAM, DECEMBER 1965

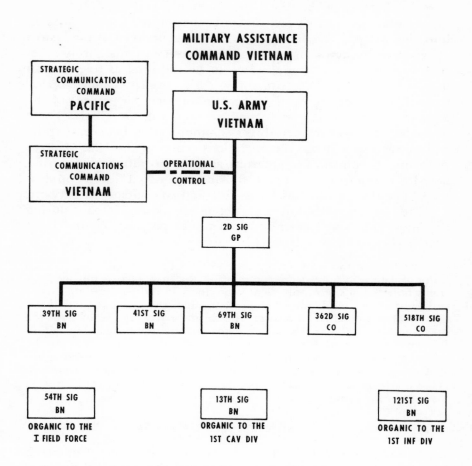

Impact of Circuit Shortages on Telephone Systems

The lack of voice channels especially affected the telephone system, particularly long-distance service within Vietnam. By July 1965 there were approximately fifty military telephone exchanges in operation and most of these were manual, using a conglomeration of equipment which required operator assistance to reach any party. The 2d Signal Group at that time started to rearrange the limited trunking under a program that required switchboard operators at the numerous switchboards located throughout the country to place all long-distance calls through eight exchanges: at the U.S. Military Assistance Command, Vietnam, headquarters in Saigon, and at Tan Son Nhut, Can Tho, Bien Hoa, Nha Trang, Qui

Nhon, Pleiku, and Da Nang. This arrangement proved ineffective, however, because of the lack of trunk circuits and the ever-increasing number of manual switchboards that were being connected into the system. The inadequate trunking between switchboards grew worse as more and more general-user circuits (trunks between telephone exchanges) came to be required as sole-user on so-called dedicated circuits to support high-priority combat operations. Even as late as April 1968 approximately 85 percent of the total channels available were tied up on a sole-user basis. These dedicated circuits provided direct communication between two facilities, such as between the operations center at the U.S. Military Assistance Command headquarters and the operations center of a field force headquarters. The U.S. Air Force relied heavily on dedicated circuits and systems to provide and co-ordinate air support.

The state of general-user telephone service in Vietnam during the mid-1960s is best described in a report prepared by the Joint Logistic Review Board. It states in part:

Operators were too busy to monitor effectively their circuits. Pick-up times of 3 to 5 minutes were common on the busy boards during peak traffic hours. Thus, not only were subscribers forced to route their own calls, but after completion of the call through the first operator, if the distant operator failed to answer, the calling party could not flash the operator back but was disconnected to join the queue again, . . . This led to the situation where, while one staff officer was tying up the operator by demanding an explanation of slow service, several other staff officers were cranking their generator handles furiously trying to get the attention of the same operator so that they, too, could discuss his reasons for being asleep at his job.

Automatic Telephone and Secure Voice Switch Plans

As early as mid-1964 the U.S. Military Assistance Command headquarters and service component staffs had recognized the need for an integrated telephone network in Vietnam, including the need for direct distance dialing through automatic long-distance switches to be located at Da Nang, Pleiku, Nha Trang, and Tan Son Nhut. The rapid buildup overtook these early efforts. In September 1965, General Westmoreland's joint headquarters in Saigon restated a requirement for a general-user automatic telephone system for South Vietnam. As a result, following a conference in Hawaii at the headquarters of the Commander in Chief, Pacific, the Pacific area headquarters of the Defense Communications Agency was asked to develop a plan for automatic telephone service for Southeast Asia. The conferees had established a need for fifty-four fixed automatic dial telephone exchanges. Of these the

Army would be responsible for seventeen in Vietnam and nine in Thailand. To tie these telephone exchanges together the conferees decided that nine long-distance switching centers were required. Tentatively the centers would be at Da Nang, Qui Nhon, Nha Trang, Pleiku, Saigon, and Can Tho in Vietnam, and at Ubon, Korat, and Bangkok in Thailand. These would be automatic tandem switches—providing direct distance dialing service much like the commercial system in the United States—designed to make most efficient use of the scarce long-distance trunks.

Earlier, in May of 1965, the Army Signal Corps planners in Vietnam and at U.S. Army, Pacific, headquarters in Hawaii had realized that automatic dial telephone exchanges were needed immediately in South Vietnam. A proposal was promptly made to the Department of the Army in Washington that, as an interim measure, fifteen 400-line transportable dial telephone exchanges be provided. As stated in the 1965 History of U.S. Army Operations in Southeast Asia:

. . . [the staff at Headquarters, U.S. Army, Pacific] realizing that procurement of fixed plant equipment and the construction necessary to house such equipment would be unable to keep pace with the expanding communication requirement, developed criteria for a model transportable dial central office, and recommended that . . . [Department of the Army] expedite design, procurement, and fabrication of the transportable offices for early shipment to . . . [Southeast Asia].

As a result of these actions Department of the Army in late 1965 ordered shipment of two fixed dial telephone exchanges, one of 2,400 lines for Cam Ranh Bay and another of 1,200 lines for Qui Nhon, and approved procurement of twelve more fixed dial exchanges and six 600-line transportable exchanges. In addition six large Army manual switchboards, modified for use as manual long-distance switchboards, were scheduled to arrive by January 1966, and would provide long-distance service until the automatic tandem switches became available.

Besides these large requirements for general-user service, there was also an urgent need for certain subscribers to be able to discuss classified matters over the telephone system. Installation of a secure voice switchboard was begun in Saigon on 22 September 1965 and the board became operational on 18 October when the first subscribers were tied in. By December 1965 this system, which consisted of seventeen subscribers in Vietnam, was completed. Voice-scrambling to frustrate enemy interceptions had hitherto been limited to a few fixed installations because of the complex and costly equipment. But there was a pressing need for its application to mobile radio, too. In the mid-1960s, secure voice equipment was for the first time programmed for the voice radios used by U.S. combat troops. The 2d Signal Group, whose many varied tasks included the distribution and maintenance of U.S. Army cryptographic material and equipment in Vietnam, began instruction on the repair of combat voice security equipment in early August 1965.

Fragmented Communications Control Is United

During the fall of 1965, as the overtaxed U.S. Army Signalmen toiled to provide the best communications support possible with their limited resources, it became more and more apparent that the command and control arrangements over U.S. Army Signal troops and systems in Vietnam were not responsive to operational requirements because they were not unified or single. These arrangements, as previously discussed, charged two separate U.S. Army Strategic Communications elements in Vietnam, both under command of their headquarters in Hawaii and both subject to Defense Communications Agency direction, with responsibility for long-lines circuits in Vietnam. Neither of these elements was operationally under General Westmoreland. Moreover, the 2d Signal Group, which was responsive to the U.S. Military Assistance Command and which came under the command and control of Commanding General, United States Army, Vietnam, had responsibility for the tails of the long-lines system over which numerous Defense Department circuits were extended to the customers. In short, the circuits and systems were intertwined but their command and control were divided.

Major General Walter E. Lotz, Jr., who served as General Westmoreland's communications-electronics staff officer from September 1965 to August 1966, described this fragmentation. He said:

A number of sites were occupied jointly by . . . [U.S. Army Strategic Communications Command and 2d Signal Group] units. When failures occurred in circuits transiting the systems of both, each unit pointed its finger at the other. . . . When a facility failed, determination of what circuits had been affected was primarily determined by the complaints of the operators at the circuit ends, rather than from circuit records, . . . ; . . . when circuits also traversed cable systems installed by base commanders, problems were further compounded. As a result of these frustrations, I wrote a message which General Westmoreland dispatched to the Army Chief of Staff, recommending common command and control of the . . . [U.S. Army Strategic Communications Command and United States Army, Pacific] theater Signal elements in South Vietnam.

General Westmoreland's message, dispatched to General Harold K. Johnson, Army Chief of Staff, on 19 October 1965, after outlining the fragmentation of the organization and control of the U.S. Army Signal troops in Vietnam, declared:

Consider it urgent to resolve fragmentation of command and control of Army Signal Units in . . . [Republic of Vietnam] to ensure communications system is responsive to operational requirements, has unity of management and control and efficiently utilizes marginally adequate resources. . . . I believe extraordinary measures required. Signal Officer, . . . [U.S. Army Vietnam] should exercise operational control over all . . . [U.S. Army Vietnam and Strategic Communications Command] elements in . . . [the Republic of Vietnam].

A Department of the Army team, headed by Major General John C. F. Tillson III, which included representatives from Headquarters, U.S. Army, Pacific, at once hurried to Vietnam in November to examine the situation and discuss the matter with General Westmoreland. As a result, on 1 December 1965 the Department of the Army placed the Strategic Communications Command's elements in Vietnam under the operational control of the Commanding General, U.S. Army, Vietnam. The Department of the Army further directed the Commander in Chief, U.S. Army, Pacific, General John K. Waters, and Commanding General, U.S. Army Strategic Communications Command, Major General Richard J. Meyer, to provide a plan whereby all Army Signal elements down to field force level would be placed under a U.S. Army Signal Command, Vietnam.

Summary, 1962–1965

From the time the 39th Signal Battalion arrived in Vietnam in 1962 through the turbulent year of 1965, the U.S. Army Signal Corps troops were continually responding to changing situations and requirements. Even from the early days in 1962 much of the communications support had to be improvised. Although plans, concepts, and programs were taking shape during the first big buildup year of 1965, actual resources in the theater remained limited and the communicators were hard pressed to provide adequate service to the customers. There was no established commercial system in Vietnam to fall back on, as there had been in Europe in World War II. In October 1944, only four months after the Allied troops invaded Europe, the rehabilitated civil system yielded about 3,000 circuits, totaling over 200,000 circuit miles, supplemented by about 100,000 circuit miles of new construction built by the signal forces of the U.S. Army.

Bunkered Communications Site in the A Shau Valley *as portrayed by Signal soldier-artist.*

By the end of 1965, however, Army signalmen were being trained and new units formed in the United States for deployment to Vietnam. These would be available in increasing numbers to upgrade and expand the improvised communications support then available in Vietnam. At the same time, as communications resources built up, the divided or fragmented control over U.S. Army communications was being corrected. The logistical and administrative troops, who were most affected by the lack of adequate communications services, would benefit. And although the over-all communications did not meet all theater requirements, combat operations were sufficiently supported in every undertaking. General Westmoreland stated in a personal message to all of the communicators in South Vietnam during the fall of 1966:

. . . The communications system, despite the handicap of having to provide more service than in any previous war and of operating under severe geographical and tactical equipment limitations, has responded brilliantly to the burgeoning requirements of a greatly expanding fighting force. No combat operation has been limited by lack of communications. The ingenuity, dedication, and professionalism of the communications personnel are deserving of the highest praise.

PART TWO

THE BUILDUP CLIMAXES, 1966 - 1967

CHAPTER III

Creation of the 1st Signal Brigade: Organization and Operation

General Westmoreland has referred to 1966 as "The Year of Development" for the U.S. forces in the Republic of Vietnam, and most assuredly it was for the Army communications effort. Yet the technical developments during the expansion of communication services at that time, although significant, were overshadowed at first by the attention given at the highest levels of Army command to eliminating the fragmented control that hampered the communications effort in the Republic of Vietnam.

Crucial Decisions

The decision by the Department of the Army at the turn of 1965–1966 to return the Strategic Communications Command's Vietnam signal elements to the operational control of the Commanding General, U.S. Army, Vietnam, was made in direct and immediate response to General Westmoreland's "fragmentation" message of 19 October 1965. This arrangement, however, was recognized by the Army as only temporary; further organizational effort was required to attain a completely satisfactory solution. General Creighton W. Abrams, Vice Chief of Staff of the Army, therefore asked U.S. Army, Pacific, in co-ordination with the Strategic Communications Command, to develop a plan for the organization of a U.S. Army Signal Command, Vietnam, to include not only all signal units of U.S. Army, Vietnam, above the field force level, but also elements of the Strategic Communications Command that were in Vietnam. General Abrams further specified that this new command be headed by a brigadier general who would serve in a double or dual-hat capacity, both as communications-electronics staff officer for the U.S. Army component in Vietnam and as the commanding general of the new communications command. Colonel Robert D. Terry, who was shortly to become a brigadier general, was given the two jobs.

U.S. Army, Pacific, completing the plans early in 1966, recommended the formation of a signal brigade to be assigned to the Stategic Communications Command but to come under the operational control of U.S. Army, Vietnam. To implement this proposal, the Department of the Army on 1 April 1966 authorized the activation of the Strategic Communications Command Signal Brigade, Southeast Asia. Later, on 26 May 1966, the embryo unit received its ultimate designation, 1st Signal Brigade.

Thus a single, unified structure to control and direct U.S. Army communications effort in the Republic of Vietnam was authorized for the second time. Previously, in 1962, all communications responsibility had rested with the 39th Signal Battalion. But events and decisions had outdated this organization and restructuring was overdue. The signal command as formed in 1966 not only gave communications responsibility in Vietnam a new direction, but also closed a major gap that had existed between signal units and managers of communications throughout Southeast Asia.

The 1st Signal Brigade soon grew larger than a division, becoming the largest signal organization by far in the history of the U.S. Army. Brigade headquarters in its first four months grew from an austere three officers to a strength of about two hundred. The first troops the brigade acquired were those of the 2d Signal Group. On 1 July 1966, Brigadier General Robert D. Terry reorganized the fledgling command by limiting the 2d Signal Group's responsibility to the III and IV Corps Tactical Zones only and by charging the newly arrived 21st Signal Group with communications responsibility in the I and II Corps Tactical Zones.

Thereafter, as new signal units arrived in Vietnam for assignment to the brigade or were activated in Vietnam, General Terry incorporated them in either the 21st Signal Group in the north or the 2d Signal Group in the south. And arrive they did. By the end of 1966 the 2d and 21st Signal Groups each comprised six battalions and each totaled well over 5,000 men.

Communications Support for Army and Corps Areas

These units of the 1st Signal Brigade maintained the area communications systems throughout the country. The area communications system is a concept whereby a signal unit, within its geographical area of responsibility, provides support to all military units—Army, Navy, Marine, Air Force, or Coast Guard—that require communications-electronics to supplement their organic capability. The U.S. Army Signal Corps refers to this service as the Army Area Communications System; however, the U.S. Army,

Vietnam, changed the designation to Corps Area Communications System in order to identify more closely with the geographical areas being served, that is, the four corps tactical zones, which were redesignated in 1970 as military regions.

Signalmen of the 2d and 21st Signal Groups operated message centers and telephone switchboards, maintained extensive networks of radio relay systems, and constructed telephone cable and wire lines between and within the increasing number of Army bases. The area communications system in Vietnam departed from the Army's signal doctrine based on the grid concept. There were reasons for this variation. First, the area communication paths either connected regional nodal centers or extended the tails to isolated elements that were not organically self-sufficient. Second, the geographical distribution of base camps and other vital installations dictated a linear, rather than a rectangular, arrangement. The classic grid advantage was preserved, however, by the brigade's capacity to provide alternate routing between key points.

With the relief afforded by both the increase in signal troops and the establishment of even a partial corps area communications system, the vital matter of communications in support of the military advisers could finally be taken up. Before the end of 1966, General Terry had assigned a signal battalion to support the U.S. advisory elements in each of the four corps tactical zones, providing area communications support for the advisers and for the South Vietnamese Army divisions. These important signal battalions were the 37th Signal Battalion in the I Corps Tactical Zone at Da Nang, the 43d in the II Corps Zone at Pleiku, the 44th in the III Corps Zone near Bien Hoa, and the 52d in the IV Corps Zone at the provincial capital of Can Tho in the Mekong Delta.

Two battalions of the 2d Signal Group had missions that differed from the rest of the units in the corps tactical zone signal groups. The 40th Signal Construction Battalion was unique within the U.S. Army; the 69th Signal Battalion (Army), because of its size and responsibilities, became the nucleus of yet another signal battalion.

The 40th Signal Construction Battalion, the only heavy communications cable construction battalion in the active U.S. Army at that time, arrived in Vietnam in the fall of 1966. The battalion immediately dispersed its companies and construction platoons the length and breadth of South Vietnam. By the end of 1970 this remarkable unit had installed over 500 miles of multipair cable within military cantonments under the most trying conditions that can be imposed by both enemy and friendly forces, having to cope

SIGNALMEN OPERATE A POSTHOLE DIGGER AT CHU LAI, *where cable telephone poles are being installed.*

with the Viet Cong's mortars and rockets and the Army's ubiquitous bulldozers. Bulldozers used in construction work invariably uproot or knock down more cables and wire lines or poles than are destroyed by enemy action.

The Saigon area had the largest aggregation of headquarters, camps, and stations in the land. The installation and operation of the myriad of communications in support of this area was the taxing job of the 69th Signal Battalion after its arrival in late 1965. When the development of the huge Long Binh military complex in October 1966 necessitated communications support for Long Binh Post, the 69th Signal Battalion was assigned the job. The battalion consisted of five signal companies, each organized to provide a specific communications service. Because of the distance involved from the 69th's home station in Saigon, it was necessary to station at Long Binh Post detachments from each company of the battalion. Since command and control problems resulted from this arrangement, the brigade commander decided to form two battalions from the assets of the 2,000-man 69th Signal Battalion. Reorganization was completed on 15 August 1967, with the 44th Signal Battalion gaining the personnel and equipment of the 69th's assets at Long Binh. It also acquired the mission of providing communications support for the Long Binh complex, including the headquarters of the U.S. Army, Vietnam, and cryptologistic support for the entire country. The 69th Signal Battalion retained the responsibility for signal support in the Saigon area, including the headquarters of the U.S. Military Assistance Command, Vietnam.

Both the 69th and the 44th Signal Battalions were assigned to Colonel Blaine O. Vogt's 160th Signal Group, which had arrived in Vietnam in the spring of 1967. This group headquarters, in addition to assuming the job of area and headquarters support assigned to the 44th and 69th Signal Battalions in the Saigon–Long Binh areas, was to control and direct other important communications activities in Vietnam. The 40th Signal Construction Battalion with its cable construction mission was assigned to the 160th Signal Group. The group reorganized and molded into an effective operation the U.S. Army's countrywide communications security logistics support activities. Another traditional Signal Corps responsibility, that of audio-visual (photographic) support, was given to the 160th on a countrywide basis. This task included backup combat photographic support to the field forces and to divisions which had their own organic audio-visual facilities. And finally the 160th assumed the responsibility for the operation of the

Southeast Asia Signal School, which had been established in June of 1966.

By the end of 1967 these three groups of the 1st Signal Brigade controlled and directed an even dozen battalions. The 2d and 21st Signal Groups provided the area communications support in the four corps tactical zones; 160th Signal Group provided headquarters support in the Saigon and Long Binh area, as well as cable construction, photographic, and communications security logistics support throughout the country.

The circuits and lines of the Corps Area Communications System operated by these groups merged at many points into the large backbone system, known from 1966 as the Integrated Wideband Communications System. This long-haul system was operated by thousands of men from the 1st Signal Brigade who were organized into battalions that constituted the U.S. Army Regional Communications Group in Vietnam.

Regional Communications Group

The U.S. Army Regional Communications Group evolved both from the U.S. Army Strategic Communications Command, Vietnam, set up in 1965 by Lieutenant Colonel Jerry Enders, and from the gateway facilities at Phu Lam and Nha Trang, which had remained under the command of the Strategic Communications Command, Pacific, until the 1st Signal Brigade was organized on 1 April 1966. The big communications facilities and systems operated by these organizations were tagged as "fixed" and were often spoken of as "long-lines." As early as February 1966, Colonel Robert D. Terry and his planners were considering a Long-Lines Group to operate the gateway facilities at Phu Lam and Nha Trang and to provide the long-haul communications between Da Nang, Pleiku, Qui Nhon, Nha Trang, Dalat, Cam Ranh Bay, Phu Lam, and Vung Tau. This plan was realized on 4 July 1966 when the U.S. Army Regional Communications Group was activated. At that time, the group consisted of the Long-Lines Battalion North, later the 361st Signal Battalion, for control and management of the long-haul communications in the two northern corps zones, and the large communication facilities in Nha Trang and Phu Lam. Later, the Long-Lines Battalion South, finally designated the 369th Signal Battalion, was activated and, by December 1966, the Da Nang message relay facility became operational under the U.S. Army Regional Communications Group. All three message relay facilities were operated by battalion-size units and were in fact designated in mid-1967 as Provisional Signal Battalions Phu Lam, Nha Trang, and Da Nang.

Signal Units in Thailand

There was still another signal group under the 1st Signal Brigade—this one in Thailand. Early in 1966 Brigadier General John E. Kelsey, Deputy Commanding General, Strategic Communications Command, had visited with the Commanding General, U.S. Military Assistance Command, Thailand, Major General Richard G. Stilwell. They agreed that all U.S. Army Signal units in Thailand should be organized into one signal group. This group was first designated Strategic Communications Command Signal Group, Thailand, under the command of Lieutenant Colonel Harold J. Crochet, and was organized to be effective 1 May 1966. It acquired all U.S. Army communications facilities in Thailand. The group was redesignated in September 1966 as the 29th Signal Group, under the command of the 1st Signal Brigade in Saigon, but remained under the operational control of General Stilwell, the top U.S. commander in Thailand. Later, in mid-1967, this operational control passed to the Military Assistance Command's Army component, U.S. Army Support, Thailand.

Thus a dual-hat role evolved in Thailand as well as in Vietnam; the senior signal commander in each country also served as the principal communications-electronics staff officer for the Army component commander. The 29th Signal Group's organization and concept of operation was similar to that of its parent unit, the 1st Signal Brigade. By the end of 1967, the group consisted of the 379th Signal Support Battalion and two provisional support companies to provide the required area communications support in Thailand; the 442d Signal Battalion, a long-lines unit, to operate and maintain the wideband communication links and sites in Thailand; and two provisional battalions to man the large message relay facilities in Bangkok and Korat.

By the end of 1967 the troop units of the 1st Signal Brigade consisted of twenty-one battalions organized into five groups and totaled about 20,000 men. Nearly all of these units arrived or were activated in Southeast Asia in the short period from April through December 1966.

The Signal Brigade in 1967

These units of the 1st Signal Brigade, along with the combat signal battalions, companies, and platoons organic to the fighting

GENERAL TERRY VISITS THE 2D BRIGADE, 25TH INFANTRY DIVISION

forces, furnished the vital communications needed to support expanding operations in Southeast Asia. The huge buildup of U.S.
and other Free World Forces had resulted in an unprecedented de-
mand for communications, from long-haul data circuitry to combat
radio nets, taxing the resources of both the signal battalions of the
combat forces and the 1st Signal Brigade.

CHAPTER IV

The Evolving Concept for Communications

As Conceived in 1966

At the beginning of 1966, there were two Army divisions and three separate infantry brigades in South Vietnam as well as a larger number of combat support and combat service support units. Headquarters, I Field Force, Vietnam, under the command of Major General Stanley R. Larsen, controlled the U.S. Army combat units deployed in II Corps Tactical Zone. The 1st Infantry Division controlled those in the III Corps Tactical Zone. At that time except for signal and aviation units, there were no U.S. Army combat units in the I and IV Corps Tactical Zones, although the 1st and 3d Marine Amphibious Divisions were in the I Corps Tactical Zone. The major U.S. Army units in Vietnam by January 1966 were the 1st Infantry Division with its 121st Signal Battalion, the 1st Cavalry Division with its 13th Signal Battalion, and the 173d Airborne Brigade. U.S. Army strength in Vietnam was to more than double in the course of 1966, increasing from approximately 117,000 to 245,000 troops, with most of the buildup occurring in the last five months. Commensurate increases took place in the other services; total U.S. armed forces in Vietnam were to grow from 184,000 to almost 400,000 by the end of 1966.

The planning that had been undertaken in late 1965 for an additional field force headquarters culminated in the activation of Headquarters, II Field Force, Vietnam, in early 1966, located with its assigned corps signal battalion, the 53d, at Long Binh. This new combat headquarters controlled the U.S. forces in III Corps Tactical Zone. Joining the 1st Infantry Division in III Corps Tactical Zone that year was the 25th Infantry Division with its 125th Signal Battalion from Hawaii and the 199th Light Infantry Brigade, which was based at Long Binh. The 4th Infantry Division and its 124th Signal Battalion joined the 1st Cavalry Division in II Corps Tactical Zone under the control of I Field Force. The extensive logistics base that was established to support the continually increasing combat forces, combined with the military emphasis during 1966 on search and destroy operations, had a distinct influence on forecasting communications requirements and molding the concept that evolved to satisfy those requirements.

Determining Communications Requirements

Prior to the major buildup phases in 1965, communications planning was based on a rather primitive, yet necessary, methodology. The communicator, not being able to determine requirements from any other sources, was literally required to draw circles or "goose eggs" around a population center or a land area and then estimate the probable troop density within that area. With these figures in mind, the planner then calculated the number of telephones which were needed. This logically led to local switchboards needed and to long-distance circuitry, for which larger multichannel systems would naturally be required. This process went on much like the words in the old song "foot bone connected to the ankle bone, the ankle bone connected to the knee bone, the knee bone connected to the thigh bone. . . ." Considering the circumstances, the communications planners did well, for no precedent existed and little doctrine was available to tell commanders, at any level, what their communications requirements would be in a counterinsurgency situation, particularly in support of administrative and logistic operations. However frustrating this method was for the signal planner, it did furnish the means to determine the needs for signal troop units that arrived in 1965 and 1966 and was the basis for the planning of the large, fixed wideband communications system.

Such "crystal ball" methods inevitably resulted in a practice that unfortunately persisted throughout the Vietnam years—the practice whereby the communicator was forced to determine his own requirements and then present them to the commander for approval. Since the communicator, the man who works in the communications field, is responsible for service, it was only logical that he did not want to fall short of the commander's requirements, which were generally unknown until his dissatisfaction was expressed. This practice, then, contributed directly to uncontrolled inflation of communications requirements. Excessive requirements, in turn, contributed to continual requests for additional resources to satisfy the requirements.

In short, the faucet had been turned on, and it was rather difficult to turn off. Colonel Frank K. Gardner, a senior Army communicator intimately involved with the early planning, put it this way in an Army War College study he wrote in 1969:

Most of the problems in Southeast Asia were caused by the great quantities of communication channels requested . . . and required by the users. For example, it was common practice in Southeast Asia to provide 32 channels of communications to a combat brigade. During the Korean War, it was standard practice to provide eight channels of communications from a Corps to a Division, while in World War II the objective was to attempt to provide four channels of communications from a Corps to a Division.

It was in the dual environment of relatively stable base camp existence on one hand, and with the massive search and destroy operations during which combat commanders often located their headquarters at remote jungle sites on the other, that the mingled fixed plant and mobile military communications facilities, the original "make-do" arrangements, were feverishly unscrambled, improved, and integrated. The first hastily improvised terminals were gradually replaced by permanent fixed facilities of the highest quality. The entire communications plant began to be upgraded and enlarged since much greater capacity was everywhere demanded. All the systems had to be interconnected and brought under better management and control to insure the utmost in service, even amid the hazards and destruction of war.

Evolution of Three Systems in Vietnam

Within Vietnam three types of communications systems evolved during 1966. All were eventually interconnected and, as far as possible, technically integrated. Each system, however, was controlled and managed separately before the creation of the 1st Signal Brigade and its dual-hatted commander. The three systems were the Defense Communications System, the Corps Area Communications System, and the Combat Communications System.

The Defense Communications System, which provided long-distance, jointly used telephone, teletypewriter, and data facilities throughout the republic, was controlled in Southeast Asia by the Defense Communications Agency, Southeast Asia Mainland Region. This joint service, regional, communications operations center in Vietnam was unique in that it exercised "operational direction and management control" over a communications system within a combat zone. One of the functions, often considered the primary function, of the agency was to respond to the communications requirements of the commanders of the U.S. Military Assistance Commands in Vietnam and Thailand. Accordingly the Defense Communications Agency, through the regional operations center in Saigon, controlled the Defense Communications System in Vietnam for General Westmoreland and later for General Abrams.

It should be noted, however, that while this regional element of a joint service agency was thus responsive to the joint U.S. commander in Saigon, its communications management philosophy and command came from the top level Defense Communications Agency in Washington, under the Department of Defense. Further, in the exercise of its management functions, the Saigon office was authorized to deal directly with the lowest communications operation levels of the operating command—the technical or facility controller. To compensate for this out-of-channel procedure, a coordination channel was established between the agency in Southeast Asia and the 1st Signal Brigade in order to keep each informed as to what the other was doing.

Except for a very few facilities operated by the Air Force and Navy, the entire operation and maintenance of the Defense Communications System in Southeast Asia rested with the U.S. Army's 1st Signal Brigade. In order to operate the system effectively, it was apparent that the brigade must also exercise the function of management. The Department of the Army letter of 25 February 1966, which approved the signal brigade concept, stated that there would be a single Army manager for the Integrated Wideband Communications System in Southeast Asia.

From the outset two organizations, the Saigon office of the Defense Communications Agency and the 1st Signal Brigade, were thus set up to manage the fixed communications in Vietnam. The extent and intensity of management differed between the two organizations and there was no gross duplication of effort, although the possibility was certainly present. Brigadier General Robert D. Terry attributed the harmony to the vigorous control exercised by the staffs of the top military commands in Vietnam and Thailand and the co-operation of the Defense Communications Agency's elements in both countries.

The Corps Area Communications System supplemented combat communications, provided extensions for the fixed Defense Communications System, and interconnected geographical areas not served by the wideband system. Over-all management of the Corps Area System was exercised by U.S. Army, Vietnam, through its operational control over the 1st Signal Brigade. In December of 1965 two signal battalions, the 39th and the 41st, had had sole area communications responsibility throughout Vietnam. But as U.S. combat forces continued to build up in the Republic of Vietnam, additional communications were urgently required to supplement the organic communications of field force, division, and separate brigade. The nature of the combat operations required the establishment of communications between division and brigade base camps as well as between the actual combat command posts located at remote landing zones and fire bases. The wide dispersion of both logistic and combat forces increased the need for interconnecting communications facilities.

One of the most pressing tasks for the 1st Signal Brigade was to insure that the rapidly growing area communications system was installed and operating effectively. In the spring of 1966, this task was virtually impossible because of the accelerated rate of the deployment of combat forces to Vietnam and the delay in the deployment of separate signal support companies and battalions. The 1st Signal Brigade was at first hard pressed to provide even barely adequate base camp and area support. In many cases organic signal units of the combat forces were required to provide base camp support, thereby reducing their ability to support combat operations. But this potentially serious problem was eased as area communications support continued to improve throughout the latter half of 1966.

The arrival of signal units from the United States during this period increased the 1st Signal Brigade's capability to the point where, in late 1966, the brigade had enough battalions to provide and manage adequately area communications support in Vietnam. The Saigon and Long Binh area of responsibility was shared by two battalions and the remainder of Vietnam was divided among nine area support battalions of the brigade. In the course of one year, area communications support had skyrocketed from the limited capabilities of only two battalions in 1965 to the total resources of two signal group headquarters and eleven battalions in late 1966.

The combat systems, which provided communications for the fighting units using organic communications equipment, were of course controlled by the tactical commanders. At one time there were sixteen interconnected U.S. Army combat communications systems in Vietnam: those of the two field forces, one corps headquarters, the Capital Military Assistance Command in the Saigon area, the seven divisions, and the five separate brigades or regiments.

CHAPTER V

Communications Operations in Combat

Supporting the Field Forces

The 54th and 53d Signal Battalions, supporting I Field Force at Nha Trang and II Field Force at a base camp called Plantation near Long Binh, were corps signal battalions, modified to operate in Vietnam. The main command posts of both the field forces, unlike those of corps, were semipermanent and did not deploy. There were also other differences between the operations of a field force and a doctrinal corps, and these differences were reflected in the communications that were provided to field force headquarters and corps headquarters in Vietnam.

The principal peculiarity of field force signal communications resulted from the need to supplant traditional wire with mobile multichannel radio relay systems across the miles that separated the base camps of the subordinate units. Multichannel radio systems were extended to lower levels than ever before. In some instances, multichannel service was provided as low as artillery battery level whereas, by accepted doctrine, normal corps systems terminate at artillery group level. Both corps signal battalions were capable of operating approximately eighteen multichannel radio relay links. It was normal to connect all U.S. combat troops and those of Free World Military Assistance Forces within the field forces' tactical areas of responsibility with the field force headquarters. In addition, it was common practice to employ circuits and systems of the 1st Signal Brigade's Corps Area Communications System to provide alternate routing.

Each of the two field forces had a distinct and separate method of employing the resources of the Corps Area Communications System to supplement the organic communications; each had a specific reason. The II Field Force, operating in the relatively flat and populous III Corps Tactical Zone, used the corps area circuitry as alternate routing for its own combat system. In essence, the Corps Area Communications System and the II Field Force's combat communications system were interconnected throughout III Corps

HON CONG MOUNTAIN SIGNAL SITE, *focal point for integration of 1st Cavalry Division communications and 1st Signal Brigade's Corps Area Communications System.*

Tactical Zone to the extent that each system could potentially provide 100 percent backup for the other.

On the other hand, I Field Force had the responsibility for II Corps Tactical Zone, which consisted of about one-half the area of the Republic of Vietnam, the largest and most mountainous tactical zone in the republic. Neither the 54th Signal Battalion of I Field Force nor the 1st Signal Brigade's corps area communications resources in II Corps Tactical Zone could alone provide the necessary command and control communications from I Field Force headquarters in Nha Trang to the various U.S. and other Free World Military Forces combat headquarters in the zone. Therefore a concept evolved under which the 54th Signal Battalion would provide the multichannel communications from the forward command post—be it a newly created landing zone for a multibrigade operation or a remote fire support base occupied by an artillery group—to a communication complex of a 1st Signal Brigade unit. From there the communications would traverse the Corps Area Communications System to Nha Trang and into the I Field Force headquarters. The alternate routing or backup capability that prevailed in III Corps Tactical Zone existed only within the Corps Area Communications System in the II Corps Tactical Zone.

Supporting the Divisions

The combat communications systems of each division in Vietnam differed from the standard doctrine in separate ways. These departures from doctrine came about partly as the result of the difference in terrain and operating conditions throughout the country and partly because of the fact that each division was, in essence, "writing its own book" on counterinsurgency warfare. The order during 1966 was "search and destroy" and each combat division had its own way of conducting such operations. As a result, during the Vietnam War the various division signal officers continually tailored their signal battalions and adjusted their methods of operating.

During the period 1969–1970 when I enjoyed the pleasure of hosting a countrywide Signal Officers' Conference, I was constantly amazed and impressed at the divergence of opinion that appeared in any discussion regarding the solution to a common problem. This can be attributed not only to the different circumstances in which each senior communicator found himself, but also to the inventiveness and free thinking that the signalman has always displayed.

For the most part, each division signal battalion in action in Vietnam had the same mission. All these units were responsible for providing the command and control communications to the division's maneuver elements, to the direct support elements, and to the combat elements of the Free World Military Assistance Force operating in the division area. In addition, the signal battalions were required to use division resources to provide communications facilities in the various base camps, complementing those provided by the Corps Area Communications Systems, which handled the bulk of the administrative and logistical traffic.

In the Republic of Vietnam a division usually operated in an area of responsibility covering 3,000 to 5,000 square miles. Such an operating area was enormous as compared to the 200 to 300 square miles in which a U.S. Army division would operate in conventional warfare. In addition, the divisions in Vietnam frequently established battalion-size and occasionally company-size fire support bases, all of which had to be tied together with reliable, responsive communications to ensure quick reaction in an emergency. As often as not, the division had the job of tying in Vietnamese Army elements, Special Forces camps, and U.S. advisers at province and district headquarters, so that mutual support was possible. The need to tie in all of these, while dealing with the factors of varying terrain and weather, made the provision of effective communications a challenge to each division. Brigadier General William M. Van Harlingen, Jr., Assistant Chief of Staff for Communications-Electronics at U.S. Army, Vietnam, from July 1967 through January 1969, stated in his debriefing report of January 1969, that the "division signal problems in South Vietnam bear little resemblance to those in a more conventional war."

The mobile multichannel radio relay system was the backbone of division communications. Generally found in a division area were a dozen or two multichannel radio relay links that connected the headquarters with brigade and battalion command posts and fire support bases. As in the field force systems, the sole-user circuit requirement was extensive. On the average, approximately one-third of the total available circuits were restricted to sole-users, and the majority of these terminated at the division tactical operation centers. For alternate emergency routing of circuits, the divisions utilized the corps area communications systems wherever and whenever possible. During combat operations, when maneuver elements initiated their action from established base camps, the mobile radio relay links were extended to the area of combat action. Alternate routing and backup links were used extensively, and the field force and the corps area communications systems often provided needed assistance, especially for intelligence, logistic, and administrative communications.

In division signal battalions, personnel and equipment authorizations were modified in order to meet the huge requirements placed on them, but in all cases a great deal of support was necessary from the corps area communicators. The necessity to rely on the Corps Area Communications System for additional support was particularly true of the austere signal battalions of the airmobile divisions, which were streamlined lightweights designed for mobile, nomadic operations, but were caught instead in the semipermanent environment of combat support and fire support bases.

Special Forces Communications in Vietnam

U.S. Army Special Forces were first employed in Vietnam in 1961. In the early stages of U.S. involvement in Vietnam, small detachments were deployed on a six-month temporary duty basis with a larger detachment based in Saigon as the control element. The mission of the U.S. Special Forces was to recruit and train Vietnamese irregular paramilitary forces to defend their own homes and hamlets. In 1964 the 5th Special Forces Group was deployed to Vietnam. This group, headquartered at Nha Trang with the Vietnamese Army Special Forces, had detachments spread throughout the country at the most isolated villages and hamlets, working with and advising the Vietnamese local defense forces. As more and more conventional U.S. troops arrived in Vietnam, the U.S. Army Special Forces effort expanded. By June 1966 the Special Forces had operational control of over 40,000 Civilian Irregular Defense Group troops and advised 35,000 members of the Vietnamese Regional Forces and Popular Forces.

To support the countrywide U.S. Special Forces mission, the signal company of the 5th Special Forces Group established secure radio teletypewriter links from the operational base at Nha Trang to the detachments and teams in each corps tactical zone. This primary system was supplemented by long-distance voice radio nets that virtually blanketed the country.

The U.S. Special Forces communications system was not the subject of much fanfare in Vietnam and was overshadowed by the elaborate fixed communications installations that appeared throughout the country. It is significant, however, that the long-distance high-frequency voice and teletypewriter radio nets of this system were the only means of contact with the outside world for many small Special Forces detachments. The communications operated and maintained by the signalmen of the 5th Special Forces Group were independent of any other U.S. system in Vietnam.

Communications for the Battle for Dak To

What happened in the battle for Dak To, near the Cambodian border in central Vietnam in November 1967, illustrates not only the responsiveness of the U.S. combat communicator during a fluid and furious engagement, but also the interconnection and mutual support which the division and field force signal battalions and the 1st Signal Brigade's area battalions continually provided for each other throughout the Vietnam War.

The battle of Dak To was not a separate operation in itself but occurred within the boundaries of the U.S. Army 4th Infantry Division's Operation MACARTHUR. Nevertheless, the size of the two opposing forces, the length and violence of the engagement, and the over-all significance of the battle have made the events that occurred in the vicinity of Dak To from late October until 1 December 1967 among the most significant that occurred in the Central Highlands.

In late October U.S. reconnaissance revealed the presence of the North Vietnamese Army's 1st Division, with its four regiments supported by a rocket artillery regiment, deployed between Dak To and the common border area of Vietnam, Cambodia, and Laos. U.S. intelligence information pointed toward an imminent North Vietnamese Army attack on Dak To. To meet this threat, Major General William R. Peers, Commanding General, 4th Infantry Division, on 1 November sent his 1st Brigade with an attached battalion of the 173d Airborne Brigade to positions just west of Dak To.

When immediate contact was made with the enemy and heavy fighting ensued, the I Field Force commander, Lieutenant General William B. Rosson, provided General Peers with more troops and support. The remainder of the 173d Airborne Brigade arrived in the Dak To area on 5 November. The next day the 4th Infantry Division established a tactical command post at Dak To to control the two subordinate headquarters. The buildup of forces, which included significant numbers of combat support and logistic units, continued until the 18th, when Colonel Donald V. Rattan's 1st Brigade, 1st Cavalry Division, joined the battle, establishing its battlefield command post at Polei Kleng, near Kontum. By then the fighting was spreading to the west as the North Vietnamese forces were destroyed or pushed back into their sanctuaries in Cambodia and Laos. (*Map 4*)

The furious action around Dak To during the month of November, together with the fact that a force of U.S. combat and support troops constituting more than a complete U.S. division had been committed, posed some problems to the 4th Infantry Division signalmen. For example, while the 124th Signal Battalion, commanded by Lieutenant Colonel William M. Spitz, was busy establishing a complete division communication system in the Dak To battle area, it also had to maintain its previously established network at Pleiku and take care of the rest of the division area in II Corps Tactical Zone. The enemy made sure that his presence would not be forgotten elsewhere by stepping up attacks by fire and ambushes throughout the entire Central Highlands. In a classic example of combat communications support, the 124th Signal Battalion successfully met the challenge by judicious use of its own resources, as well as those provided by I Field Force's 54th Signal Battalion and the 43d Signal Battalion of the 1st Signal Brigade.

The 124th's initial effort in support of the battle of Dak To

FIRE SUPPORT BASE ON A RIDGE NEAR DAK TO. *Tall antennas were used to extend range of mobile voice radios.*

was the installation of two 12-channel links from the division main command post at Camp Enari near Pleiku to the division's 1st Brigade forward command post at Dak To. Upon arrival of the division tactical command post at Dak To, on 6 November, the battalion was operating a mobile, one-position switchboard for the 1st Brigade of the 4th Division. With the increase in activity it became necessary to install a second switchboard for the division tactical command element. This second switchboard, like the first, was shortly saturated; it became apparent that the 1st Logistical Command's forward support activity, airfield control personnel, and other support units, continually arriving by air and road, all had a need for area communications support. The Division Signal Officer made a request to Headquarters, I Field Force, for area service in order to relieve the increasing pressure on his two small mobile switchboards and the command and control teletype circuits which his signal battalion had activated. As a result, the 1st Signal Brigade's 43d Signal Battalion, under the command of Lieutenant Colonel Edwin B. Gentry, installed area telephone and message

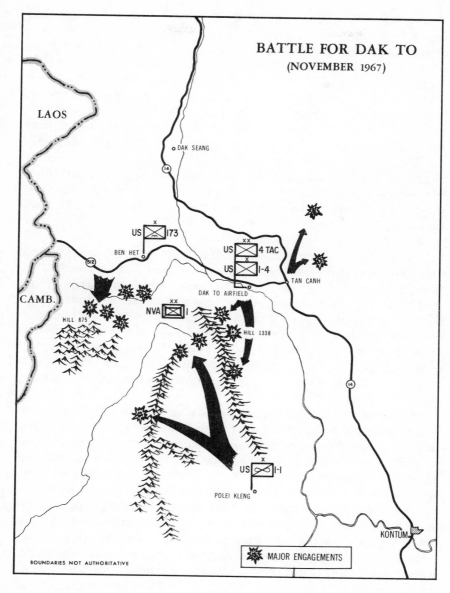

BATTLE FOR DAK TO
(NOVEMBER 1967)

LAOS

o DAK SEANG

US ⊠ 173
BEN HET

US ⊠⊠ 4 TAC
US ⊠ 1-4
TAN CANH

DAK TO AIRFIELD

CAMB.

HILL 875

NVA ⊠⊠ 1
HILL 1338

US ⊠ 1-1
POLEI KLENG

KONTUM

BOUNDARIES NOT AUTHORITATIVE

✹ MAJOR ENGAGEMENTS

MAP 4

service at Dak To as well as a 12-channel general-user link from Dak To to Pleiku. Thus relieved of area service responsibility, the communications resources of the 124th Signal Battalion could and did remain oriented toward the command and control effort.

As the 173d Airborne Brigade, commanded by Brigadier General Leo H. Schweiter, arrived, it was tied into the system. The 124th installed the necessary links between the division tactical command post and the 173d's battlefield command post at Ben Het, west of Dak To. To provide the circuits from the 173d forward command post back to its aviation support, which remained at Kontum, and its base camp location at An Khe, a mix of 124th, 43d, and I Field Force's 54th Signal Battalion multichannel links was employed. Lieutenant Colonel Robert M. Springer's 54th Signal Battalion provided a multichannel link between Dak To airfield and Kontum. At Kontum this link tied into an established 43d Signal Battalion system to pick up the An Khe circuits. Two other 54th Signal Battalion links already in operation, one from Camp Enari to Pleiku and one from Pleiku to Dak To airfield, were used for additional special purpose circuitry.

Some of the largest demands for circuits over the systems provided by these three battalions were to support U.S. air operations. Not only was there a need for extensive communications at the Army airfields but there was also a requirement for air route traffic control and point-to-point close air support circuits. Finally, significant numbers of channels were needed to control and guide the large bomber effort directed by General Westmoreland. The extensive requirements for communications in support of air operations were not confined to this battle, but were typical of most other operations in Vietnam.

As the battle reached a peak in mid-November, the area system between Dak To and Pleiku proved insufficient. The 1st Signal Brigade thereupon made arrangements to install a 24-channel tropospheric scatter system with mobile equipment between Dragon Mountain, adjacent to Camp Enari, and the U.S. advisers' compound, which stood next to the village of Tan Canh and had been consistently used as a radio relay site into the Dak To airfield. Of these twenty-four channels, the 124th Signal Battalion was to use twelve in direct support of the 4th Infantry Division. In order to extend these circuits to the division tactical command post at the airfield, the 124th's linemen installed a 12-channel landline carrier system using spiral-four cable. This four-mile link was one of the relatively few cable systems installed outside the perimeter of U.S. camps in Vietnam. Usually radio relay would have been used, but in this case the 4th Infantry Division signalmen had simply exhausted the supply of radio equipment.

In all, during the thirty-three days of the battle for Dak To, over fifteen multichannel links were installed and operated in direct support of the operation. The majority of these belonged to the 124th Signal Battalion. Without the help and assistance of the communicators from the I Field Force and the 1st Signal Brigade, however, the support provided the combat and the combat service commanders during this significant battle would have been very lean at best.

CHAPTER VI

Control and Direction: Problems and Solutions

The size and complexity of the communications systems in Southeast Asia, along with the fact that the systems were frequently interconnected and superimposed, required the formation of special organizations, techniques, and procedures to furnish effectively communications engineering and technical control and direction for the systems. This is sometimes referred to as technical management.

Technical Management

Technical management of the combat systems was comparatively simple because of the generally uniform system configurations and small size of the networks. The engineering and technical control functions were built into the operating unit, and over-all direction came from the unit's operations staff. Each signal battalion of the field forces and divisions had a systems control section, popularly referred to as SYSCON. The section was in operation twenty-four hours a day, usually with two men on each shift. The systems control section was responsible for engineering and controlling all of the communications systems and networks operated by the unit.

The chain of technical management of the defense and corps area communications systems, however, was long, and, like the Mekong River, followed myriad paths. The chain for both systems began outside Vietnam. That for the 1st Signal Brigade originated at the Army's Strategic Communications Command Headquarters at Fort Huachuca, Arizona. Technical control and direction for the Defense Communications System went from the Defense Communications Agency in Washington to its Pacific Area in Hawaii, then to its Southeast Asia Mainland Region in Saigon. The Army aspects of the communications engineering and controlling efforts, rather than those of the joint Defense Communications Agency, are emphasized here.

When it was formed, the 1st Signal Brigade inherited the engineering and control tasks that always accompany any large head-quarters charged with communications system installation and operation responsibilities. These tasks had previously been performed by Colonel Moran's 2d Signal Group systems control and engineering staff. To this small organization had fallen the chores of engineering and controlling all 2d Signal Group installations and operations at a time when the group consisted of about 3,000 men spread thinly throughout the republic.

In the spring of 1966 when Colonel Robert D. Terry was organizing the 1st Signal Brigade, the growing communications activity in Vietnam required separate, sizable, headquarters elements. Each engineering speciality would have its own headquarters element—one for fixed-plant projects, another for the Integrated Wideband Communications System under construction and still another for telephone management. Similarly, centralized control over both Department of Defense and Corps Area Communications Systems required a separate, complex structure in the brigade headquarters. Elaborate equipment was needed in addition to a large, highly specialized work force of skilled communications controllers.

Communications Engineering and Installation

On 23 April 1966, Colonel Terry addressed a memorandum to his brigade deputy, Colonel Gordon B. Cauble, to Colonel Moran, and to Colonel Riley, Deputy U.S. Army Vietnam Signal Officer, on the subject of plant engineering and installation functions. He proposed that a communications engineering management agency be established composed of seventy-five men. A month later, on 23 May, the organization was set up as the Communications-Electronics Engineering and Installation Agency, responsible for developing the required plans and programs and providing the management of fixed-plant projects, especially heavy cable construction in Vietnam. Lieutenant Colonel Clarence R. Driscoll came to the 1st Signal Brigade from the Pacific field office of the Strategic Communications Command's worldwide Engineering and Installation Agency on Okinawa. He arrived in Saigon in June 1966 to run Colonel Terry's engineering agency, bringing six engineers with him. By March 1967 he had sixty-six engineers at work in the agency. Before the end of 1967 the agency was enlarged still further and was renamed the Communications Systems Engineering and Management Agency. One of the most important elements of this agency was the project management office for the Integrated Wideband Communications System being installed in Southeast Asia. Originally headed by Lieutenant Colonel Patrick F. Kearins, this office was the focus for co-ordination between the contractor and the military services.

Telephone Engineering and Management

Another managerial element, also involving engineering duties, was the brigade headquarters organization that supervised the installation of telephone switches in and around Saigon. To supervise the mushrooming number of telephone switches in the metropolitan area, Colonel Terry created the Saigon Telephone Management Agency. In the summer of 1965 the U.S. military telephone system in Saigon had consisted of two manual switchboards that served the two separate joint U.S. headquarters complexes in the Saigon area. The total telephone cable facilities, or outside plant, at that time consisted of approximately 400 circuit miles of combat field wire, spiral four, and rubber-covered 5- and 26-pair cables. In addition, three cables systems were leased from the Vietnamese Postes, Telegraphs et Telephones office to provide circuit-routing between Saigon, Tan Son Nhut Air Base, and the 1st Signal Brigade's terminal at Phu Lam.

The number of U.S. Army telephone switchboards in Saigon was increased during the fall and winter of 1965 to six local manual telephone exchanges, three other small manual exchanges called private branch exchanges, and one long-distance switchboard connected into the countrywide system. Two of the manual exchanges were made up of large, nine-position switchboards mounted in vans. The remaining switchboards consisted of components of an older model, manual telephone central office, with four to nine operator positions, depending on the location.

As the need for more land for U.S. activities increased, so did the telephone requests. These six local exchanges no longer provided "on base" communications; instead, a U.S. Army metropolitan telephone system began to take shape. This system lacked an over-all manager and, as a result, several serious problems arose. Greatest of these problems were inadequate trunking, and in some cases none at all, between local exchanges; lack of an outside cable plant capable of meeting increasing subscriber demands; lack of unified cable and circuit records; and insufficient operator positions to handle traffic during the busy hours. At this time the nine-position switchboard vans were handling an average of 1,800 calls during their busiest hour. To further complicate the telephone communication picture, Saigon had two civilian and four Vietnamese Army dial telephone exchanges, a U.S. Air Force exchange at Tan Son Nhut Air Base, and three exchanges operated

SIGNALMEN OPERATING A LARGE MANUAL TELEPHONE SWITCHBOARD AT SAIGON

by the U.S. Embassy. The U.S. Army telephone system was superimposed on these existing facilities. With this maze confronting it the Saigon Telephone Management Agency was established and began operations in April 1966.

The inadequate manual facilities had to be replaced. The 1st Signal Brigade performed this task by providing automatic dial telephone switches, mounted in huge vans and serving up to 600 subscribers. Later, fixed automatic dial telephone exchanges were installed. The latter exchanges were sophisticated modern facilities, serving several thousand subscribers. Since these modern automatic telephone projects were being installed in the capital area they had to be interconnected by large, high-capacity cable links or trunks of high quality.

In the spring of 1966 these projects were the responsibility of the telephone management agency and were largely confined at first to the metropolitan area of Saigon. But as 1967 progressed, the need for automatic telephone service expanded far beyond Saigon. Automatic dial telephone facilities were installed at many outlying points, not only in Vietnam but also in Thailand. The 1st Signal Brigade found it necessary to set up a telephone management office in each numbered signal group. Since telephone service was required beyond the confines of the automatic dial service provided to local areas, automatic long-distance dialing facilities were needed also. These last military sophistications were called tandem switches by the Army, but were better known in the United States as direct distance dialing.

Obviously the telephone management agency, the over-all control in the brigade, had to redouble its engineering and management responsibilities. By the end of 1967, therefore, it was enlarged and redesignated as Southeast Asia Telephone Management Agency. The accomplishments of the telephone agency and the workers of the brigade were most immediately evident in the metropolitan area. During the first nine months after the agency's formation, 90 percent of the telephone system in Saigon was transformed from a manual to an automatic dial system. Although there had been many problems, they had been solved; and now the single-manager concept pioneered by the Saigon Telephone Management Agency was being broadened to include telephone management for the entire country.

Communications Control Means and Methods

Within the first week after the creation of the 1st Signal Brigade, Colonel Terry had issued a letter of instruction, dated 7 April 1966, concerning communications control. The objective of communications control as he defined it was "to provide daily operational direction of the communications circuits which collectively form the U.S. Army Communications Systems Vietnam and Defense Communications System (DCS Army) circuits in Southeast Asia." The organization that was created to perform this function was originally called the Command Communications Control Center Agency. It utilized the resources and the operating personnel of the 2d Signal Group systems control element.

These men of Colonel Moran's 2d Signal Group had been performing communications control duties in Vietnam since mid-1965. In August 1965, when the U.S. Army Strategic Communications Command had become responsible for the Defense Communications System in Southeast Asia, it also became responsible for controlling the circuits of the Defense Communications System. The 2d Signal Group systems control had then continued to watch over only the combat and corps area circuits. This split responsibility had produced problems on procedures for reporting circuit failures, activations, and similar routine communications actions. Combining the communications control of the Defense Communications System and the corps area circuits was, of course, one of Colonel Terry's major objectives.

A crucial and central organization in this unifying effort was the new communications control agency, which was renamed in February 1967 the Army Communications Operations Center in Saigon. The center served as the primary control hub for all Army Southeast Asia communications. A secondary control center was established in November 1966 in Thailand at Korat. The center received up-to-the-minute information and data on all systems, their operation, and message traffic loads and flow. In particular, the center's operators watched for any breakdowns, or "outages" in communicator jargon, and insured that proper action was taken. This service was the Army's contribution to the Defense Communications Agency's management over the Southeast Asia Wideband System. Besides this major over-all center in Vietnam and a secondary center in Thailand, there were similar, smaller system control elements within the 1st Signal Brigade's numbered groups, watching over area communications. Within the signal battalions of these groups were still smaller watchdog elements. This was also true of the combat signal battalions of the divisions and corps.

These agencies of the communications community were all established to provide the essential engineering and control efforts necessary to manage the communications network as it existed in the spring of 1966. All the agencies were eagerly anticipating the long-awaited Integrated Wideband Communications System which would give the country the fixed-station, high quality backbone so urgently needed for effective command control.

CHAPTER VII

Integrated Wideband Communications System

The Integrated Wideband Communications System was a microwave and tropospheric scatter communications web that eventually spanned the entire Republic of Vietnam and Thailand. The equipment was commercially procured, installed by a contractor, and the system was, therefore, of commercial fixed-station improved quality throughout. It constituted the Southeast Asia portion of the global Defense Communications System which had been delegated to the Army by the Department of Defense through its Defense Communications Agency. The completed system became by far the largest communications complex the Army had ever undertaken, creating an equivalent of the Bell Telephone System for South Vietnam and Thailand. However, the integrated system did not come into being quickly, easily, or, for that matter, inexpensively.

An urgent request for the fixed-plant system had been made in mid-1964, accompanied by a required implementation date of December 1965. The implementation date, however, was not met; in fact, fifteen months elapsed from the date of the contract award until the first link became operational in December 1966. This initial link was a small part of Phase I of the three ultimate phases of the Integrated Wideband Communications System.

The Three Phases

In Vietnam, Phase I of the Integrated Wideband Communications System, incorporating and expanding the BACK PORCH links, was primarily intended to provide more circuits from Saigon and north throughout the country. A new extension was built from the Monkey Mountain site in Da Nang to Phu Bai, a large U.S. encampment area just south of the imperial city of Hue. In the center of a huge triangle between Saigon, Nha Trang, and Pleiku, an important circuit and system-switching facility was built on top of Pr' Line Mountain, a short distance to the southeast from Dalat. High-capacity links were to be provided between Pr' Line and the

PR' LINE MOUNTAIN SIGNAL FACILITY, *a key site of the Integrated Wideband Communications System.*

three corners of the triangle. Numbers of short links were built in and around the capital city area, where the fixed systems of Phase I replaced earlier tactical microwave circuits. Phase I of the integrated system was not intended to support a large troop buildup but was to provide the communications for up to 40,000 U.S. troops in Vietnam, primarily advisers and helicopter units.

As the force level in Vietnam grew, the requirements increased, and General Westmoreland's communicators were forced to ask for the Phase II upgrade. The Department of Defense approved Phase II in January 1966 and scheduled its completion for October 1966.

The primary purposes of Phase II were to expand both the major north-south backbone trunk system and the Saigon microwave complex, and to extend the fixed-plant system into new areas in support of combat operations. Sixteen new sites were to be added, involving twenty-five new communications links; nine Phase I links were to be upgraded to a higher capacity. In all, the total number of terminals was doubled, and the circuit total was tripled. When the Saigon–Nha Trang tropospheric scatter link was upgraded to carry 240 channels, it was the world's first tropospheric scatter link to achieve daily operation at so large a capacity.

In August 1966 the Secretary of Defense approved Phase III of the Integrated Wideband Communications System, which would provide support for 400,000 troops. The primary objective of this phase was to extend the wideband system into the Mekong Delta area in order to meet the needs of expanding combat operations there. No new major relay systems were included in this phase, but many short links were added around large nodal sites in the existing wideband network. The first link of Phase III would not be completed until December 1967.

Concurrent with the award of a letter contract to Page Communications Engineers, Inc., for the Vietnam portion of the fixed-plant system, the Army awarded the contract for the Thailand portion to Philco-Ford Corporation. In Thailand progress was made in the same phase pattern as in Vietnam. With the obvious exception of combat action, the problems experienced in Thailand during the ultimate completion of the wideband system paralleled those in Vietnam.

Problems and Delays

The installation project moved forward relentlessly, if somewhat unevenly at times, amid diversified problems and difficulties of funding, managing, supplying, and manning, which invariably accompany any large-scale effort. This effort, however, was unique in Army experience for its size and complexity. Implementation of such an ambitious project could not be expected to come easily. Construction and operation at the many sites, ultimately fifty-nine sites in Vietnam, fell short of the expected timetable. This situation was hardly surprising in view of such serious obstacles as remote sites and transportation difficulties in Southeast Asia and funding and programming delays in Washington. In retrospect, it is to the credit of everyone involved that the undertaking turned out as well as it did.

Because of these delays, Phase I and II were not completed on schedule. The last link of Phase I was not accepted by the government until January 1968, two years and one month after the original requested operational date of December 1965. Not until February 1968 did the last link of Phase II go into operation in Vietnam, a year and four months after the date requested, October 1966. The remainder of the Integrated Wideband Communications System, Phase III along with a few additional modifications, would not be completed until much later in 1968. In the meantime, commanders at all levels urgently demanded that the system be completed as soon as possible.

Such demands for the completion of the system, however, could not be easily met. The military had chosen to install a fixed, commercially procured system. And the commercial equipment needed for this system was entirely different from the communications hardware previously used in a war zone; it was custom built and enormously costly. In addition, engineering, manufacturing, testing, acceptance, and operation presented many difficulties at all levels. But it was the great expense of the system which surprised and chagrined many.

At Army and Department of Defense levels in Washington, the major impediment was getting money. The time-consuming process of funding had to come before anything else could be done. The budgetary mills of government could only grind out the funds slowly by increments. Yet, piecemeal funding, and the resultant bit-by-bit contracting and installing, apparently cost more in the long run than a single lump-sum allocation at the outset. For example, a Strategic Communications Command report dated 7 June 1967 states, in part: "This office has received a retransmission from Page Communications Engineers, stating that existing Phase III money would be exhausted by 15 July 1967 and that if additional incremental money was not forthcoming, the program will suffer in increased cost."

In mid-1966 the Assistant Secretary of Defense had returned a third addendum of the wideband communications program to the Defense Communications Agency for additional justification. The authorities in Washington were questioning the need for all the money that was being sought for channel expansions of trunks not yet in service and replacements of mobile combat systems at greatly increased capacity. They disbelieved the reports and requirements coming from the Southeast Asia war zone and insisted that the funds be minutely justified. The requirements had to be stated in detail, despite the fact that no one could determine the precise requirements far in advance. Frequently, changes had to be made in the system—in such matters as site location, equipment, and number of circuits—during the process of contracting and even of construction. Unforeseen demands continually arose requiring changes and, usually, expansion, even after installation had begun or had been completed. Not until May 1966 were the Phase I and II contracts with Page Communications Engineers, Inc., finally "definitized" for Vietnam. And four months earlier, Phase III had already been launched, calling for more circuits, more terminals, and the upgrading of older terminals. This phase involved more equipment and larger antennas to provide more channels, resulting naturally in a plea for more money.

The increases and changes occurring in the midst of the funding and approval process were not the result of inefficient planning. Rather, because of the graduated nature of the troop buildup and the constantly changing situation caused by combat activities, the volume and type of traffic and the disposition of subscribers were not known early enough or in sufficient detail to enable proper engineering of the trunking system. The logical steps in fixed-plant network engineering—traffic, plant, transmission, and equipment engineering—could not be followed in this case.

The difficulties encountered in obtaining adequate funds and establishing firm requirements were not the only factors contributing to the delays in the fixed communications project. From the very beginning of the program, problems of site concurrence and site access were almost endless. For isolated sites, the problem was especially time-consuming, beginning with the initial engineering surveys to find suitable locations. There were delays in getting aircraft and ground transport to remote areas in order to survey hilltop sites, and to make tests to determine the adequacy of proposed radio paths. Time was also consumed in obtaining permission from the local government to use these sites. Other delays ranged from the care required to avoid desecrating sacred trees in Thailand to the payment exacted for future harvests in Vietnam.

Site acquisition difficulties involving the terminals on bases already established were often only a matter of building space. In many cases, installation commanders who had agreed to furnish space were not able to do so when the time came for construction. These commanders discovered that their own unanticipated expansion had taken all of the available space. In addition, the space requirements for the system increased beyond original estimates. Buildings had to be erected, and in some cases expanded, to meet new requirements.

Production capacity and shortage of materials for the wideband system constituted another significant problem area. There were approximately 150 U.S. subcontractors providing material for the fixed communications in Vietnam and 100 subcontractors for Thailand. Page and Philco-Ford, the prime contractors, made every effort not to engage in direct competition for equipment by avoiding whenever possible the same vendors. In many cases, however, these prime contractors found themselves inadvertently competing with one another because the second-, third-, and fourth-tier vendors were furnishing components to the principal subcontractors for each. In addition, procurements by other government agencies with equal or higher priority than the Integrated Wideband Communications System as well as increased purchasing by commercial firms saturated the market. The industry was saturated to such a point that even the offer of premium prices could not cause delivery dates to be moved up. Business was so good that many firms refused to accept a contract or subcontract with a penalty clause. In many cases, subcontracts were awarded to firms that offered the earliest delivery dates and not necessarily to those with the lowest prices; however, the majority of suppliers failed to meet promised delivery dates. The basic causes of these failures were the delayed delivery of components or raw materials and the shortage of skilled labor.

The transportation of material, once it was finally available, was one of the most serious problems in the program. The accelerated buildup in Vietnam caused seaports and airports to become congested with cargo of every type imaginable destined for the war zone. Special-mission aircraft was the only means of getting the fixed communications hardware to Southeast Asia quickly. Throughout the period of installation, the U.S. Air Force Military Airlift Command provided special flights to bring the sorely needed electronic equipment into Vietnam. In addition, because a very active war was being waged and ground movement was constrained, the Air Force combat cargo aircraft and the Army cargo helicopters were often the only means of getting the hardware to the sites.

Site construction was accomplished in a variety of geographical and geological areas that include the rice paddies of the Mekong Delta, the mountainous, rocky mid-country region, and the sandy beaches along the coast. Each location presented a unique problem. Building and antenna foundations in the delta area had to be of a spread-footing design to prevent sinking in the water-soaked clay of the rice paddies. In sandy areas, the problem of soil erosion was so severe that it frequently appeared to defy solution. The very pronounced wet and dry seasons in Southeast Asia also controlled construction schedules. It was virtually impossible to accomplish any outside construction on communications sites during the rainy seasons.

Other problems affecting construction of the wideband system were the remoteness of some sites and the security restrictions at practically all sites. Army cargo helicopters were used extensively

A 120-FOOT ANTENNA FRAME UNDER CONSTRUCTION ON VUNG CHAU MOUNTAIN, QUI NHON

to transport men and material to mountain sites such as Pr' Line, Hon Cong Mountain near An Khe, and VC Hill at Vung Tau. Often considerable stretches of new road had to be built even before the actual work could begin. Use of the Vung Chua Mountain site, for example, just north of Qui Nhon, required the construction of thousands of feet of new road. In addition, an enormous amount of rock and dirt had to be removed from the site in order to provide a flat surface on which the facilities could be built.

In the latter months of 1966 additional delays and difficulties in construction and installation were caused by enemy action. Earlier, the big military communications sites had remained remarkably free from enemy harassment. It was almost as if the enemy favored the new communications services which Southeast Asia was receiving for the first time in its history.

On Thanksgiving Day 1966, however, a costly ambush of a communications equipment convoy occurred near Dalat in the hills of south central Vietnam. The convoy, manned by 1st Signal Brigade soldiers and contract civilian workers, was attacked while

COMBAT SOLDIERS OF THE 1ST SIGNAL BRIGADE FIRING MORTARS FROM
PR' LINE

en route to the mountaintop site at Pr' Line. Eight Page employees and one 1st Signal Brigade trooper were killed and eleven men were wounded. Two of the soldiers in the convoy, Staff Sergeant Gerald H. Bamberg and Specialist Walter S. Rogers, were cited for valor in holding off the enemy and preventing the complete annihilation of the convoy.

Another major attack affecting communications facilities occurred on the night of 26 February 1967 at Da Nang. The enemy launched a large surprise rocket attack against the Da Nang Air Base. One of the first enemy targets was the Army's signal compound on the base. Fortunately there were no casualties, but the rockets completely destroyed four vans in the communications complex which housed the temporary mobile message relay facility. Replacement vans were rushed to Vietnam by the Strategic Communications Command's 11th Signal Group in the United States, enabling reactivation of the tape relay in ten days. Actually, no circuits or links were completely out for more than a few hours, partly because of quick rerouting of circuits and partly because the enemy had failed to damage the big radio and technical control vans located adjacent to the tape relay facility.

At last, by the end of 1966, despite all delays and difficulties, the first circuits of the wideband system were tested, accepted by the Army, and "cut to traffic," that is, put into service passing actual communications. Brigadier General Robert D. Terry accepted the first link of the Integrated Wideband Communications System on 21 December 1966. This was one of two links which carried traffic between Phu Lam and the Tan Son Nhut Air Base in the Saigon area. These were the first fixed sites completed in Vietnam. The first links in Thailand had been put into use a little earlier, on 5 November, following the completion of tests between Korat and Udorn.

After the cutover of the first links, the wideband communications system flourished, fed by the multimillion dollar contracts to civilian companies and pushed by the thousands of combat signal troops that joined the 1st Signal Brigade in the 1966–1967 period. By mid-April 1967, hundreds of circuits in the integrated system had gone into service and eleven sites had been completed in Vietnam.

Combat Mobile Equipment Used in the Interim

It should be noted, however, that because of the long delays invariably encountered since the submission of the initial require-

SITE OCTOPUS, OUTSIDE SAIGON, A MAJOR COMMUNICATIONS HUB IN 1967

ments in August 1964, the fixed communications system could not keep pace with the huge buildup of U.S. and other Free World military forces in Vietnam. Keeping in mind that Phase I of the over-all system was designed to support 40,000 troops in Vietnam and that Phase II had a ceiling of 200,000, it can easily be understood that the Army communicators had many problems when the U.S. strength alone exceeded 350,000 men the day the wideband system's first circuit was put into service.

The solution to these problems, however temporary, was to use every piece of medium and heavy tropospheric scatter, microwave, and other mobile and transportable multichannel radio equipment that could be deployed into Vietnam. Throughout the long months of delay in the fixed communications project, the buildup of troops continued as did their appetite for long-haul circuitry. Consequently, the mobile tropospheric scatter and microwave links of the Defense Communications System were rushed into service and abounded throughout the country, not only providing circuitry from the backbone system to locations that would one day be served by the fixed communications being installed, but also supplementing the backbone system itself. In October 1967, eleven months after the first fixed-plant link was accepted, approximately 70 percent of the circuits of the Defense Communications System in Vietnam were in fact provided by mobile equipment inadequate for fixed-station standards. They were operated by the corps area signal groups of the 1st Signal Brigade.

Status at the End of 1967

Regardless of the long, continued, and heavy dependence on mobile equipment for the long-haul Defense Communications System in Vietnam, enthusiasm among the customers ran high in 1967 as the fixed communications system became a reality. At mid-year in 1967, all praised the progress made by Phases I and II. Most of the basic links were in service or were being tested prior to activation. Wind-up activities of Phases I and II peaked in 1967, and by the end of November testing had begun on the final thirteen of seventy-six links. The last link of Phase I in Vietnam, between Vung Tau and Pleiku, was accepted on 27 January 1968, and acceptance of the last link of Phase II, between Vung Tau and Long Binh, followed one month later.

The total system upon completion of Phase II consisted of seventy-six communications links operating at fifty-eight sites in Southeast Asia. Of the more than ten thousand circuits, nearly all reached their destination by both tropospheric scatter and microwave radio trunks. However, a few circuits passed through a recently completed submarine cable system. This system, approved by the Department of Defense in February 1966, comprised six links, capable of sixty voice channels each, connected to the major communications sites at Da Nang, Qui Nhon, Nha Trang, Cam Ranh Bay, and Vung Tau in Vietnam, and Sattahip, south of Bangkok in Thailand. The installation was completed in May 1967. This dependable cable system, protected by its undersea route and interconnected with the fixed-station radio system at these six sites, constituted a valuable segment of the ever-growing Southeast Asia Wideband System.

Site construction meanwhile was progressing on the Phase III effort of the integrated system. Practically all of Phase III implementation occurred in 1968. While the first Phase III link in Vietnam, a 60-channel link between Vung Chua Mountain and Phu Cat Air Base, was accepted by the United States Government during December 1967, the entire system would not be completed until 1969.

CHAPTER VIII

Elaborations in the Big Networks

The big terminals of the Integrated Wideband Communications System, the huge antenna arrays, the transmitting and receiving equipment aligned row after row, the humidity-free, temperature-controlled buildings, surrounded by stacks of sandbags and revetments, the enormous, deafening diesel generators for electrical power, the hundreds of circuits constituting the Defense Communications System that laced Vietnam and Thailand—all of this would have been useless without the facilities at every site that provided the switching, or "breakout," of the individual circuits to form the myriad voice, teletype, and data networks that served the customer. The fact that a 240-channel "pipe" existed between two sites was meaningless to the combat commander who could not send a message or place a phone call between those two sites because the switches were not yet completed. The signal planners, therefore, had far more to do than just design the fixed wideband system. Concurrently with fixed-system planning and installation, efforts were being strongly directed toward improving both the telephone and message-switching service in Vietnam, where the rapid buildup had created havoc with the already overloaded military communications facilities.

The Growing Telephone System

During the 1965 buildup of U.S. troops in Vietnam, telephone systems sprang up wherever headquarters, base camps, logistics centers, and air bases were established. Originally each system was operator oriented, requiring the users to work through a manual switchboard to place a call. Such a slow inefficient system was a natural consequence of the rapid military buildup. Naturally when the 1st Signal Brigade was activated, telephone switching improvement stood high on the list of things to be done. At the outset the top requirement was meeting the needs of the Capital Military District in the Saigon area. As was pointed out previously, the evolution of telephone service in this area consisted of many manual

TEST BOARD IN ONE OF THE MANY DIAL TELEPHONE EXCHANGES IN VIETNAM

switchboards, some consolidation, and then dial service. The telephone switch upgrade program was not confined to the Saigon area. The process of replacing older, manual equipment with newer dial equipment in the Capital Military District set a pattern that was followed throughout Vietnam, and applied to military encampments throughout Southeast Asia. As the big manual switchboards were replaced in the Saigon area, they were moved to outlying camps to replace the smaller combat switchboards. Similarly, as three 600-line, van-mounted dial exchanges were replaced by fixed, commercial ones in the Capital Military District, the vans were sent out to field camps to replace manual switchboards.

To solve the immediate problems of long-distance telephone service in Vietnam, temporary arrangements were made in late 1966 and early 1967, pending the eventual installation of direct distance dialing switches. Six long-distance manual switching centers, employing large, nine-position manual switchboards mounted in vans, were established in Vietnam. Along with Saigon's long-distance switchboard the network by April 1967 was made up of long-distance switchboards at Da Nang, Qui Nhon, Pleiku, Nha Trang, and Can Tho. This interim long-distance system remained the primary means of communication for general users until well into 1969, when the direct distance dialing system became operational.

Installation of dial telephone exchanges in the north meanwhile occupied the 1st Signal Brigade's Telephone Management Agency, as well as civilians working for contractors. By the end of 1966, fixed automatic dial exchanges were scheduled for installation at fifteen different locations in Vietnam. The first conversion to a fixed-plant Army dial telephone exchange was at General Westmoreland's headquarters in January 1967. By the end of the year, eleven of the fifteen fixed-plant dial exchanges were operational. Counting all the military services, there was a total of twenty-nine fixed-plant dial central offices with over 34,000 lines in operation in Vietnam by the end of 1967.

Record Traffic: Message and Data

Another important communications network that received much attention during this period was the record or the printed message and recorded data traffic network. Use of the teletypewriter was, of course, the older method and the standby for record or printed message communications. It continued to serve as a backbone of communications into and out of the war zone, and within Vietnam as well, especially for classified information.

Along with the message system employing manual tape relay, data communications were rapidly developing in Southeast Asia, equaling and eventually exceeding the standard teletype operation. An Automatic Digital Network which could process both message (teletypewriter) and data traffic was planned and approved by the Department of Defense in 1965. Automatic switching centers were to be established at Phu Lam and Nha Trang. Together, these two centers, each with a 100-line termination capability, were to fulfill an original requirement for 130 U.S. subscribers, with a capacity of 750,000 standard-length messages per day. This capacity represented a two-fold increase over the existing manual relay network's capability.

A number of months elapsed and millions of messages were passed over the manual systems, however, before communicators in Vietnam enjoyed the benefits of the automatic network. Because of the growth in traffic volume on the general-user message network as troop buildups and wartime activities increased, the major relay

SIGNALMEN TRANSMITTING MESSAGES AT MANUAL TAPE RELAY CENTER

at Nha Trang was upgraded to a 22-line fixed installation in April 1966, and the capability of the Phu Lam facility was expanded by upgrading it to seventy-two lines by the end of that year. To handle the increased traffic in the north, a third relay facility, mounted in vans, was activated at Da Nang in the I Corps Tactical Zone in December 1966. It was at this facility that two tape relay vans were destroyed by enemy action in February 1967. The Da Nang relay station was subsequently upgraded to a 48-line fixed installation and put to use in December 1967. The signal brigade commander, General Terry, made the following comments in his letter of 21 December 1966 to Major General Richard J. Meyer, commander of the Strategic Communications Command, regarding the first Da Nang transportable relay:

The cutover of Da Nang tape relay went extremely well. Traffic was a little under 5,000 [messages] yesterday. The impact on the load at Nha Trang was also apparent since Nha Trang dropped to around

12,000. Now, if we can keep the priority on the completion of the Class IV [fixed] projects, both at Nha Trang and Da Nang, we should be able to stay ahead of the message business.

These three facilities, linked together by the wideband communications system, were capable of relaying common-user message traffic between each other, as well as from major relays outside Vietnam. In addition, the three facilities were connected to minor message relays and to area communications centers. Daily traffic volume handled by all three major facilities averaged up to 70,000 messages in late 1967.

One of the most significant problems encountered in message switching in Vietnam was the abnormal amount of traffic using high-precedence indicators. The rapid growth in traffic resulted in completely distorted precedence distribution, in which up to 50 percent of all traffic was classed as "Immediate" or "Flash." The Joint Chiefs of Staff found it necessary to adopt a "Superflash" category in order to make sure that the real "Flash" action was properly disseminated. General Van Harlingen, 1st Signal Brigade commander from mid-1967 until February 1969, noted in his final debriefing report that, as a result of the burgeoning of message traffic, there was a slowdown in the delivery of messages; and a situation had developed in which there was constant danger of losing messages. Such losses were most likely to occur during equipment breakdowns in the overworked relay centers, and led to huge backlogs or pileups of messages. During periods of heavy backlog, even meticulous attention to procedures did not always prevent errors resulting in loss. And a lost message is considered, and rightly so, one of the most grievous sins in the communications-electronics community.

The requirements for data services in Southeast Asia followed, to a large extent, the growth of supply activities in that area; and, as the logistics system began to take shape, so did the capability to provide data communications improve. At the beginning of 1966, the only data relay in Vietnam was at the Phu Lam facility. This data relay had been established to provide limited service for urgently needed general-user digital data traffic. The majority of the circuits in Vietnam that were connected to the Phu Lam Non-Automatic Relay Center could handle only ten data cards per minute, a rate that was intolerably slow to both the subscriber and the communicator and totally incapable of satisfying the growing data requirements.

Consequently, while the automatic digital switching centers destined for Vietnam were being developed and produced under government contract, upgrades and extensions of the existing manual data relay system were in progress. The Phu Lam Non-Automatic Relay Center was upgraded by mid-1967. Circuits with a capacity of passing 200 cards per minute were connected with automatic switching centers in the continental United States, Hawaii, and the Philippines, as well as 100-cards-per-minute circuits to ten manual data centers in Vietnam. A second manual data relay, at Nha Trang, was cut to traffic in August 1967. Combined, these two facilities of the 1st Signal Brigade handled an average of 830,000 data cards per day. Although the non-automatic relay centers provided some relief for the three major tape message relays in handling their high volume of traffic, the equipment was still manually operated, thus requiring a large number of operators, and causing excessive handling time and a high rate of error. Unfortunately the message and data situation would not be rectified until the Automatic Digital Network was installed in Vietnam in mid-1968.

The Secure Voice Network

By mid-1967 still another communications improvement was being made in Southeast Asia by the Army and the 1st Signal Brigade. The recently developed and highly sophisticated Automatic Secure Voice Communications System was being installed in the Defense Communications System to serve not only Vietnam and Thailand, but also the armed services throughout the world. This system, a vital military requirement, took a considerable amount of time and effort to develop, for the feat involved more than the scrambling of voice impulses prior to transmission, a technique used to a limited degree during World War II. It was necessary to develop compact equipment that could be widely used, either in a spacious military office or in the dusty hot tent of a combat commander in a war zone.

A less sophisticated predecessor to this secure voice system, the "Talk Quick" system developed by the Navy, had been used in Vietnam since late 1965. Automatic Secure Voice System implementation, to replace "Talk Quick," had been planned in several phases. Phase I provided fof 200 secure voice subscribers in Vietnam. On 17 July 1967 the first element of the Vietnam portion of the Automatic Secure Voice System became operational—an automatic dial exchange serving fifty secure voice subscribers in Saigon. Installation of the remaining 150 subscriber lines and attendant small manual switching centers serving all of Vietnam was planned for early 1968. This sophisticated equipment, although it satisfied

TRANSMITTING DATA CARDS AT NON-AUTOMATIC DATA RELAY CENTER

operational needs, required much patience and training to use and maintain.

All of these networks, the telephone, the record message and data, and the secure voice networks, were built and improved during 1966 and 1967. It was not until 1968, and in some cases 1969, that they were completed.

Space Age Communications

Communications between Southeast Asia and the rest of the world received another boost during the period 1966–1967. U.S. Army communicators, in conjunction with the National Aeronautics and Space Administration, had devoted the past several years to improving and refining the embryonic art of satellite communications. Although limited satellite communications had existed in Vietnam and Thailand since 1964, a much more reliable system with greater capacity was required. In January 1966 the Defense Communications Agency published a plan to give communications satellites a larger role in support of the war effort. Thirty-two satellite communications paths were planned between Southeast Asia, Hawaii, and the continental United States. These paths were divided between two satellite communications systems, the Initial Defense Communications Satellite System and the commercial system of the Communications Satellite Corporation.

The Initial Defense Communications Satellite System called for developing and launching a score of satellites to serve fourteen earth terminals. The satellites were placed in random distribution, in near-synchronous equatorial orbits a little more than 21,000 statute miles above the earth. Two of the fourteen earth terminals, with a total capacity of twenty-two voice channels, were installed in Vietnam: one at Ba Queo, near Saigon, and the other at Nha Trang. These satellite communications terminals went into operation in July 1967 with ten of the planned twenty-two voice channels accepted for use: five from Saigon to Hawaii and five from Nha Trang to Okinawa. By the end of 1967 the two Vietnam terminals were totally operational, and had been upgraded to their maximum capacity of eleven voice channels each.

In addition to the twenty-two military-owned and military-operated voice channels going into Vietnam, the Defense Communications Agency also leased from the commercial Communications Satellite Corporation ten other channels to complete the thirty-two channels required for Southeast Asia. These channels, which terminated at Bang Pla, just southeast of Bangkok, Thailand, were accepted for use in May 1967. Extension of six of these ten channels from Bang Pla to Vietnam was accomplished via the submarine cable link from Thailand to Vung Tau, where they interconnected with the wideband communications system in Vietnam.

On the last day of 1967 the original satellite communications system, called SYNCOM, which was near the end of its expected life cycle, went out of use in Southeast Asia. At that time the experimental satellite over the Pacific area lost its usefulness and the old SYNCOM earth station at Ba Queo was closed. This forerunner of modern satellite communications had been pressed into service during a crisis when no one could be sure that it would work at all. It performed admirably, however, and for three years the experimental satellite communications system provided a vital link between the war zone and Washington, D.C.

The National Military Command and Control System

The years 1966 and 1967 saw a dramatic increase in the combat efforts in Vietnam by both U.S. and Free World Military Assist-

CONSOLE OPERATOR AT SAIGON SATELLITE TERMINAL. *Soldier monitors satellite traffic and selects satellite to be used.*

ance Forces, whose strength in Vietnam jumped from just over 200,000 in January 1966 to well over half a million by December 1967.

U.S. Army combat forces in Vietnam were bolstered by the arrival of the 9th Infantry Division at the turn of 1966–1967 and the 101st Airborne Division in December 1967, reuniting the 101st with its 1st Brigade, which had been in Vietnam since mid-1965. Another major Army combat force to appear was the 23d Infantry Division, American. This division, activated in Vietnam during September 1967, eventually controlled the 11th, 196th, and 198th Light Infantry Brigades. It was supported considerably during the organizational phases by the resources of the 1st Signal Brigade. This support was in the form of a rapidly organized signal unit, which was subsequently designated the American division's organic 523d Signal Battalion. At the same time, Army signal troops, which were to provide the communications for this combat force, went from 7,500 men to over 23,000 in the 24-month period.

But numbers alone do not tell the story. It is essential to understand the unprecedented concepts and working agreements that were developed to control and direct the communications effort, and to realize the extent to which the Defense Communications Agency, the Army's Strategic Communications Command organization, and the combat division and corps communicators had to merge their philosophies of operation and adjust their thinking to cope with the mission at hand. U.S. communications experience in the Vietnam War quite effectively redefined two words in the dictionary of communications—mobile and fixed. At one time these words brought to mind distinct and separate images that were the opposite of each other, but now in Vietnam fixed communications and mobile communications merged.

The Vietnam conflict saw the first large-scale combat employment of the centralized and worldwide National Military Command and Control System of the Department of Defense. The rapid and large buildup of U.S. forces in Vietnam demanded that this system be extended to and expanded within the Republic of Vietnam. Moreover, and perhaps paramount, the U.S. Government, because of internal U.S. sensitivity to the conduct of the Vietnam War, chose to exercise close civilian control over military actions. To do this, an unprecedented communications network was established in the field and between headquarters in Vietnam and higher headquarters outside the country, in this case, specifically, the Office of the President of the United States in the White House.

To attain the highest degree of command and control possible, a vast system of communications lines was built within Vietnam, stretching to Hawaii and eventually on to Washington, D.C. Every communications method was ultimately employed, from field wires and the infantryman's hand-held radio to submarine cables and orbiting satellites. No single service or organization can take all the credit for this extensive communications network; rather, it is to the credit of all communicators, military and civilian, that by the end of 1967 a system actually existed that allowed continuous, high quality communications from the fire base to the White House.

Training the Communicator

The proliferation of commercially procured, fixed-plant, and often automated systems and equipment, as operated by the Army's 1st Signal Brigade, required trained, experienced personnel. This requirement was not, of course, limited to the fixed-sta-

COMBAT SIGNALMEN WITH TASK FORCE OREGON ON PATROL

tion troops of the signal brigade. The communicators of the fighting forces and the signal brigade's area support units also encountered equipment and procedures that were foreign to combat communications of only a few years earlier. Such equipment as the new portable and mobile combat field radios and battlefield secure voice devices, together with such innovations as dynamic and effective airborne relay to extend the ranges of radio systems, and extensive heavy cable construction on combat bases all required installers, operators, and maintenance men, highly proficient in their trades. Training soldier-technicians, always an important task in Army communications, became more pressing and more complicated in the 1960s than ever before. This situation was an inevitable consequence of the ultrasophisticated and complex systems that were brought into the theater of war. Although the use of automatic equipment does, of course, reduce the number of operators, it requires of the fewer operators more training and greater skill.

When the first commercial quality backbone systems were installed in Southeast Asia, the Army had few Regular Signal Corps troops capable of operating and maintaining the system. Short-term soldiers did not stay long enough to be trained on the job. The initial backbone terminals, therefore, and later the fixed-station additions, continued to be operated, even to the end of 1967, largely by civilian technicians of Page Communications and Philco-Ford. The presence of civilian communications controllers, maintenance technicians, and operators in a war zone, often in outlying and exposed locations, was something new in Army communications experience. It was another aspect of the unique war in Vietnam.

Ultimately, men in uniform had to be trained to do the work, however complicated and exacting and however difficult and costly the training. The cost became evident before the end of 1966. The two fixed-station prime contractors, Page and Philco-Ford, had contracted with the U.S. Government to establish complete wideband system terminals and schools at the U.S. Army Signal School, Fort Monmouth, New Jersey, to enable the Army to give soldiers adequate training. The cost to the government of these two contracts exceeded ten million dollars. The Page school was dedicated at Fort Monmouth in November 1967, and the Philco school opened a short time later. Not until well along in 1968, however, would soldiers trained in these schools arrive in Vietnam and Thailand.

Army signalmen working at the big communications terminals in the war theater were meanwhile learning their trade in an old and familiar Army manner—they were training on the job. An especially acute need for technical controllers on the wideband communications systems led the 1st Signal Brigade to establish a small school for this specialty in June 1966 under the auspices of the Regional Communications Group of the 1st Signal Brigade. Six months after the school opened, it had graduated 25 officers and 173 enlisted men to help stem the ever-growing shortage of technical controllers in the field.

The meager beginnings of the 1st Brigade signal school near Saigon, with its one course, was soon expanded both in the number of courses offered and in space and facilities. When the huge Army complex at Long Binh was ready for occupancy, the school, then known as the Southeast Asia Signal School, graduated from its one-room, country schoolhouse atmosphere and moved into the expanded Long Binh facilities. This signal training center at Long Binh was formally organized by the 1st Signal Brigade into the United States Army Training Facility, 1st Signal Brigade, in August 1968.

Although the school was a U.S. Army training facility, operated by the signal brigade, the scope of its instruction continually broadened until it included courses for all communicators and electronics men from both United States and Free World forces, from the combat surveillance radar operator and combat radio repairman to the fixed microwave operator. By the end of 1968, for example, over 3,000 students had been graduated from the school, which had by then expanded its curriculum to more than twenty different courses of instruction on mobile and fixed equipment.

Summary, 1966–1967

As 1967 came to an end, the large communications systems in Vietnam were near completion. The over-all system, lean at best just two years before, was now taking shape, and the hand-to-mouth days seemed to be on the way out. The combat communicators—the troops of the corps, divisions, and separate brigades—had gained valuable experience during their service in the war zone, and the lessons were being well applied. The helicopters and the infantryman's radio sets, in both airborne and ground configurations, had been integrated so successfully that new meaning was given to the phrase "command and control." The combat multichannel systems of the divisions and field forces were interconnected with and supplemented by the 1st Signal Brigade's Corps Area Communications System. Two of the three phases of the ambitious Integrated Wideband Communications System project were complete and in service. The combination of the fixed-plant, high quality communications links and the expanding dial telephone network lessened significantly the number of times the communicator had to hear that painful phrase "hoot 'n holler." Extensive working arrangements were in existence between the Saigon office of the Defense Communications Agency and the 1st Signal Brigade, and between the 1st Signal Brigade and the combat units. The control and direction concepts so painstakingly and, at times, painfully evolved in late 1965 and early 1966 were now bearing the fruits of success.

On the other hand, communications service was by no means perfect at the end of 1967. The long-distance general-user telephone system still relied on manual switching techniques. Message traffic in Vietnam still was sent via manual tape relays and, unfortunately, in some remote cases a personal visit was often faster than sending a message. Considerable refinements and improvements were now required in all areas of communications services. But the foundation had been built and now was the time to get about the business of major leaps forward in command control

GENERAL VAN HARLINGEN *(seated)* INSPECTS COMMUNICATIONS GEAR ON
A COMMAND HELICOPTER

communications-electronics. The enemy had been continually met
and defeated by our aggressive soldiers; relative security existed in
all the cities and around the combat bases. It was generally be-
lieved that the Viet Cong and North Vietnamese would honor
their self-declared truce during the coming February 1968 *Tet* hol-
iday.

PART THREE

COMMUNICATIONS MATURE AND MOVE TOWARD VIETNAMIZATION, 1968—1970

CHAPTER IX

U.S. Army Signal Troops and *Tet:* 1968

Hanoi Changes Strategy

During 1967 Hanoi evidently concluded that the chances for success in its campaign to control South Vietnam were diminishing. The South Vietnamese Government was becoming stabilized as a result of a new constitution and the nationwide free elections held during September and October 1967. The nation's economy and its armed forces were showing improvement. As a result of continual military pressure applied by the Free World Military Assistance Forces during 1966 and 1967, the North Vietnamese and Viet Cong forces had been compelled to withdraw from the areas close to the population centers of South Vietnam and move into their more remote base areas or their secure sanctuaries in Cambodia and Laos. Hanoi decided a major change of strategy was necessary. A large offensive would be launched in the Republic of Vietnam. At the same time the civilian population would be incited to rise up against the government and the soldiers of the Vietnam Army would be encouraged to desert. Exactly what Hanoi expected of this strategy is still uncertain. The probable intentions of the enemy were described by General Westmoreland in his report on the war in Vietnam:

He probably had many things in mind—not the least of which was the necessity to do something dramatic to reverse his fortunes. He surely hoped that his dramatic change in strategy would have an impact on the United States similar to that which the battle of Dien Bien Phu had on the government and people of France. In this way he might hope to bring about a halt of the U.S. effort and the withdrawal of the U.S. Forces.

The Tet Offensive

During late December 1967 and January 1968, Hanoi infiltrated troops and supplies into forward positions and into the population centers of South Vietnam. The offensive was launched 29–30 January in the I and II Corps Tactical Zones, and 30–31 January in the remainder of the country under cover of a seven-day truce declared by the Viet Cong for the celebration of *Tet*, the Vietnamese lunar New Year. The initial assaults, employing about 84,000 North Vietnamese and Viet Cong troops, were mounted against 42 cities and provincial capitals, 64 district capitals, and 50 hamlets. (*Map 5*) In most cities the attacks were thrown back within two or three days; in Saigon and Hue, however, the fighting was protracted. Heavy fighting also continued for sometime in Kontum, Ban Me Thuot, Can Tho, and Ben Tre. By the end of February 1968 the enemy had lost some 45,000 men killed.

During May and early June the enemy launched new attacks, primarily against the Saigon area and in the northern part of South Vietnam. Before these assaults, and after them too, a series of rocket attacks were made against military installations and in some cases rockets were launched indiscriminately against the civilian population.

By the end of June 1968 when General Abrams took command of the U.S. Military Assistance Command, Vietnam, upon General Westmoreland's departure for his new duty as the Army Chief of Staff, enemy losses were estimated at 120,000 during the first six months of 1968. The South Vietnamese had come through this major enemy offensive with more confidence, stronger armed forces, a strengthened government, and, last, a population that had disregarded the call for a general uprising.

Building Communications in the Northern Provinces

Before *Tet* General Westmoreland had initiated countermeasures while the enemy was moving into forward areas. As large numbers infiltrated into the Republic of Vietnam population centers during December 1967 and January 1968, intelligence information began to be received at General Westmoreland's joint headquarters that a major offensive was to take place. Consequently, in mid-January, General Westmoreland strengthened the U.S. forces in the Saigon area and moved the 1st Cavalry Division and elements of the 101st Airborne Division into the northernmost provinces of South Vietnam. Because of the heavy reinforcement in the northern I Corps Tactical Zone in anticipation of a major enemy offensive, General Westmoreland decided to open in late January a temporary control headquarters in that area. This forward headquarters of the U.S. Military Assistance Command, under the command of Lieutenant General William B. Rosson, was designated in March as Provisional Corps, Vietnam, and was ultimately redesignated the U.S. Army XXIV Corps. The corps

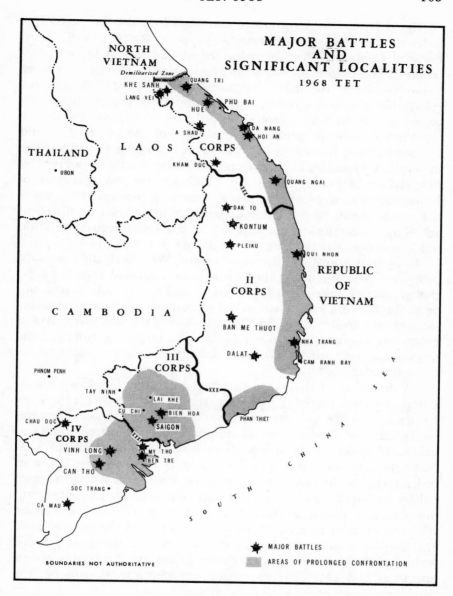

MAJOR BATTLES
AND
SIGNIFICANT LOCALITIES
1968 TET

MAP 5

was placed under the operational control of the III Marine Amphibious Force, which had responsibility for operations in the entire I Corps Tactical Zone.

By 26 January a requirement was placed on the 1st Signal Brigade to provide communications support for the U.S. Joint Forward Command Post to be located at Phu Bai. A tailored battalion of 608 officers and men had to be drawn from the existing resources of the 1st Signal Brigade. General Van Harlingen decided that the headquarters staff of the 459th Signal Battalion, then stationed at Nha Trang, would deploy to provide the battalion control element, while the remainder of the battalion would be formed from brigade resources drawn from over forty locations in South Vietnam. The first elements of the battalion arrived at Phu Bai on 28 January 1968. By 5 February the major communications services were operational at this new headquarters, while the last elements of the tailored battalion had closed by 6 February. Thus, communications support by the 459th Signal Battalion was hastily organized during the height of the *Tet* offensive.

Communications facilities for General Westmoreland's forward command post, including the existing Phu Bai dial telephone exchange, were bunkered in, or revetted, and cables were placed underground. Work continued at a fast pace despite an around-the-clock enemy rocket attack on Phu Bai during the first three days of February. Though numerous rounds landed near the sites and the revetments were hit by many shell fragments, the equipment remained undamaged.

In the midst of the battle that raged in Hue, the 459th Signal Battalion was ordered to provide secure teletypewriter message service to the fire support co-ordinator located with the Vietnamese 1st Infantry Division command post at an old fortress, the Citadel, in Hue. The only means of reaching the Citadel was by U.S. Navy landing craft, which had to traverse the Perfume River in order to reach the canal that circles the fortress. A four-man team led by 1st Lieutenant John E. Hamon was organized to move and operate the equipment. During the trip to the Citadel the landing craft came under heavy mortar attack and two of the enlisted men and the lieutenant were wounded. Lieutenant Hamon, despite his wound, and the one uninjured enlisted man put the equipment in operation and provided the critical communications support for over twenty-four hours until help arrived.

The 459th continued to provide support to the joint forward headquarters in Phu Bai until the newly arrived 63d Signal Battalion headquarters, commanded by Lieutenant Colonel Elmer H. Graham, took over the mission of the provisional organization in March of 1968.

Additional Free World Military Assistance Forces were deployed into the northern I Corps Tactical Zone during February while heavy fighting was taking place at Hue and Khe Sanh. General Van Harlingen had to further draw down from 1st Signal Brigade's resources to provide the required communications support. A signal support company, organized from his brigade's assets, had been airlifted into the area of heavy fighting in the northern provinces by the end of February. This last drain on brigade resources left little in the way of contingency assets. It was in fact necessary to deactivate twenty-one less essential radio-relay links in order to provide the required resources. A few days later, however, the 596th Signal Support Company, which had just arrived in Vietnam, was assigned to the 459th, and made a significant contribution to the battalion's communications capability.

These "draw-downs" by bits and pieces to provide the resources required in the north had placed a heavy burden on the brigade. As General Van Harlingen explained in his debriefing report: "The 1st Signal Brigade was thrown into the midst of an administrative maelstrom, with personnel and equipment attachments and all the accompanying paper storm."

U.S. Army Signalmen and Tet

The story of the 459th Signal Battalion, as it was provisionally organized and deployed, is unique since the deployment occurred as the *Tet* offensive took place. The hastily organized battalion had to respond quickly and install and operate the vital communications needed, even though it was under fire. Being under fire, however, was not new to the men of the 459th; many of them had come from other locations in Vietnam that were also under attack. At this time all the signal troops of the divisions, field forces, and 1st Signal Brigade deployed throughout South Vietnam were simultaneously installing communications in support of the combat forces and defending their positions. They were handling increased communications traffic loads that resulted from the fighting and were repairing and restoring disrupted communications services. It was commonplace that in many places signalmen had to fight and at the same time provide communications support. One element of the 1st Signal Brigade, the communications control center with its communications status-reporting system used to control and manage communications passing through more than 220 locations in Vietnam, found itself in a unique position. The reporting system was capable and did provide battle information in considerable detail concerning enemy activity to the Military Assistance Command and U.S. Army, Vietnam, operations centers.

General Van Harlingen in his after action report described the efforts of the signalmen thus:

Troops were ordered to be prepared to install and restore command and control communications while under attack in all cases. I consider it essential that the Signal troop be trained and prepared to work under fire, even when he must deliberately expose himself to do so. . . . Because of the overall quality of the American soldier in Vietnam, and, due in part to stimulation of the enemy's offensive, at no time did the Signal troop fail to come through when required. Equipment was cannibalized, antennas restored, cable repaired, isolated sites defended and new links activated both night and day during periods of intense enemy rocket, mortar and small arms fire.

Thousands of dramatic incidents, both recorded and unrecorded, occurred as the signalmen fought, in one way or another, to keep the communications "in." A few are told here as they happened during *Tet* 1968.

On 1 February, during the height of the heavy fighting in Hue, close to the Demilitarized Zone in the north, the Senior U.S. Military Officer in the besieged city considered withdrawing the signal troops of the 1st Signal Brigade's 37th Signal Battalion from the Hue tropospheric scatter site to avoid their being overrun. But General Van Harlingen knew the site was critical because it provided the main communications with the beleaguered U.S. forces at Khe Sanh. He directed Lieutenant Colonel Jerry Davis, Jr., the 37th Battalion commander, to order the men to remain at the site so that the vital link with Khe Sanh could be kept operational, and at the same time he requested immediate assistance from the U.S. Marine forces fighting near the Hue signal site. For the next thirty-six hours the small installation was surrounded. The signalmen beat off repeated assaults by an estimated Viet Cong battalion attacking with small arms, automatic weapons, and rockets. Helicopters trying to reach the surrounded signalmen were turned back by machine gun fire; it was impossible to evacuate the wounded. One soldier with a shattered arm was desperately in need of medical help. His fellow signalmen treated the wound while they received instructions by telephone from Phu Bai. Two companies of Marines, trying to reach the site from the U.S. Advisor's compound three blocks away, finally gained the signal site after thirty-six hours of fighting.

While heavy fighting was going on at the Hue tropospheric scatter site, U.S. troops near the Laotian border at Khe Sanh were under constant mortar and rocket attack. A direct hit on a bunker by a rocket killed a lieutenant and an enlisted man of the team operating the Khe Sanh mobile tropospheric scatter terminal. Three of the remaining four team members were wounded by the rocket, and two of them subsequently died from their wounds. The remaining signalman, Specialist William Hankinson, with the assistance of two U.S. Marines, kept the system on the air for forty hours until replacements arrived.

At Dalat, in the mountains of south central Vietnam, signalmen of the 362d Signal Company and Company E, 43d Signal Battalion, both attached to the 1st Signal Brigade's 73d Signal Battalion, were in continuous action from 1 through 6 February 1968. During the afternoon of 1 February members of the 218th Military Police Detachment were pinned down in their small compound by fire from an estimated two platoons of Viet Cong. Major William R. Crawford, the commander of 362d Signal Company, upon learning of the plight of the military policemen, immediately organized and led a 20-man rescue team. The small force of signalmen engaged the enemy with individual weapon and grenade fire, evacuated wounded military policemen, and laid down a base of fire that enabled the uninjured soldiers to withdraw. At the same time, inside Dalat, Captain Donald J. Choy, the operations officer of the 362d, led a heavily armed convoy to the Villa Alliance Missionary Association compound, which was surrounded by Viet Cong. The signalmen fought their way to the compound and successfully evacuated the thirty-four occupants. All told, the signal troops of the 362d Signal Company and Company E, 43d Signal Battalion, rescued and provided shelter for more than sixty noncombatants.

Incredibly, there were no serious communications failures during the first weeks of the offensive. The fixed communications site at Hue, which was operating on commercial power, went off the air late in the evening of 31 January 1968 when the power station was overrun and the backup power generators located at the site had become inoperative. Communications at the site were restored by the afternoon of 2 February after replacement generators had arrived with a convoy that had gotten through, despite two ambushes on the way.

During a mortar attack on the Phu Lam signal site close to Saigon on 8 February, a vital 50-ton air conditioner serving the large tape message relay was knocked out. For several hours the station could process only "Flash" and "Immediate" precedence traffic. After intense efforts the air conditioner was repaired and became operational the following day.

A considerable number of communications failures did occur when multipair communications cables that had been installed

CABLE TEAM AT WORK DURING TET OFFENSIVE

overhead on poles were cut or shredded by shrapnel and small arms fire. After the enemy's initial attacks, major cable failures were reported in Saigon, Bien Hoa, Soc Trang, Lai Khe, Cu Chi, Can Tho, and Ban Me Thuot. In some of these instances mobile radio systems were installed so that critical circuits could be restored. Signal cable repair teams worked around the clock to repair the damaged cables, even though they were often under enemy fire while working from exposed positions. In fact, on a number of occasions enemy snipers had to be knocked out so that the signalmen could work on the cables. One cable repairman, Specialist David J. Kubik of the 36th Signal Battalion, was suspended forty feet above ground repairing a large cable at Lai Khe when a mortar attack started. Disregarding his own safety he continued his repairs.

By 5 February most of the cables had been restored, but in the areas where heavy fighting continued, such as Saigon, numerous cables were still out. Essential communications traffic continued to flow, nonetheless, rerouted through extemporized circuits.

During the period of the heaviest attacks, 31 January through 18 February 1968, only three mobile multichannel systems operated by the 1st Signal Brigade went out because of combat damage, and then only for a brief time. Whereas the cables that had been constructed above ground were damaged considerably, those which had been buried suffered little. General Van Harlingen, commenting on the effects on communications during the first weeks of the *Tet* offensive, declared: "Miraculously, although Signal troops sustained several hundred casualties, there were no disastrous interruptions of communication at any time during the first few weeks of the offensive."

Later, however, the enemy was able to disrupt communications and inflict heavy casualties at a signal site in southern Vietnam. During the night of 13–14 May 1968 the 25th Infantry Division signal site atop Nui Ba Den, a lone mountain about forty miles west of Saigon near Tay Ninh, came under a mortar, rocket, and co-ordinated ground attack. Some fifteen signalmen of the 1st Signal Brigade were also at the site, operating corps area radio relay systems. The enemy penetrated the perimeter and severely damaged the equipment and facilities. Twenty-three U.S. soldiers were killed, three were wounded, and one was missing as a result of the enemy assault. Shortly before I arrived in Vietnam in September 1968 to serve as General Van Harlingen's deputy brigade commander, the Nui Ba Den site was again attacked, early in the morning of 18 August. Even though there were some casualties, damage was light, and the enemy was successfully repulsed.

Reorganization of Corps Area Communications

Throughout the enemy's 1968 *Tet* and summer offensives the area support battalions of the 1st Signal Brigade continued to supplement the organic communications of the field forces, divisions, and separate brigades. But even before the *Tet* offensive, it had become evident to General Van Harlingen that excessive duplication existed between the long-lines area system supporting the U.S. and Free World Military Assistance Forces and the numerous networks which had previously been installed to support the U.S. advisers. Economy and efficiency dictated their consolidation into single systems, one within each of the four corps tactical zones. This consolidation would not only promote economy in the use of equipment and manpower resources but would also increase the capabilities of the field force commander by providing communication links between U.S. and South Vietnamese units. It would provide each field force commander with a single network for control over his own troops and for execution of his mission as the Senior Advisor within his corps tactical zone.

General Westmoreland approved the concept in November 1967 and the consolidation was begun at once. Because the III Corps Tactical Zone appeared to be the one most cluttered with duplicated links, General Van Harlingen began consolidation in that area. Within the first month, his efforts netted a savings of twelve radio relay links with all their associated equipment and operating personnel. These assets immediately proved valuable in providing badly needed communications to support the 25th Infantry Division in War Zone C, northwest of Saigon, during Operation YELLOWSTONE in early 1968.

The consolidation, which streamlined the communications systems in the corps tactical zones saving a considerable number of men and much equipment, was finished in December 1968. The single system concept for support of operations in each of the corps tactical zones became the doctrine for area signal support in Vietnam. One of the more significant features of this doctrine was that the combat commanders could, in an emergency, obtain immediate communications support from the local representatives of the supporting area battalions of the 1st Signal Brigade without validation from Headquarters, U.S. Army, Vietnam. On many occasions the resulting close relationship between the brigade's area battalion commander and the division or field force for which he was providing signal support meant the difference between "go" or "no go" on short-notice combat operations.

Brigade Organization in 1968 for Area Communications

The consolidation of communications systems resulted also in more efficient disposition of personnel and equipment. Consequently, 1968 was another year of major reorganization for the 1st Signal Brigade. With the buildup of forces, communications facilities underwent further expansion, upgrading, and reorientation. During 1968 signal companies and battalions continued to deploy to Vietnam, joining the 1st Signal Brigade, while most of the signal organizations already in Vietnam were busy submitting modified tables of organization and equipment. All this reorganizational activity was a clerical nightmare, but it was unavoidable because the signal units were operating with minimal resources and, as their mission expanded, more resources had to be provided.

One of the more significant organizational changes made by the 1st Signal Brigade during this time was the activation of still another signal group, which was to operate in the I Corps Tactical Zone. As of mid-1968, the U.S. Army's XXIV Corps, commanded by Lieutenant General Richard G. Stilwell and based in Phu Bai, with responsibility for the I Corps Tactical Zone, had operational control of three U.S. divisions: the Army's 1st Cavalry and 101st Airborne Divisions and the U.S. 3d Marine Division. This corps also had close liaison responsibilities with the Vietnamese 1st Infantry Division, headquartered in the old imperial city of Hue. In July 1968 the 1st Brigade of the 5th Mechanized Infantry Division arrived in Vietnam and was also assigned to the XXIV Corps tactical area. It was soon obvious that the 1st Signal Brigade's 63d Signal Battalion was overburdened by having to provide communications support to all U.S. forces in the two northern provinces of Vietnam as well as the organic communications for the XXIV Corps.

By September 1968 it was plain that an additional signal group headquarters would be required to provide command and control of the signal elements in the I Corps Tactical Zone. The span of control within the 21st Signal Group had become too great; the group had six battalions assigned and was deployed over two-thirds of South Vietnam with a strength of about 7,000 men. Consequently, a new signal group headquarters, known as the I Corps Tactical Zone Provisional Signal Group, was formed on 8 September 1968. The staff for this new signal group was formed, as in other cases, by tightening the belt and drawing from other 1st Signal Brigade units. The I Corps Tactical Zone Provisional Signal Group, commanded by Colonel Mitchel Goldenthal, became oper-

CHART 2—1ST SIGNAL BRIGADE ORGANIZATION, JULY 1969

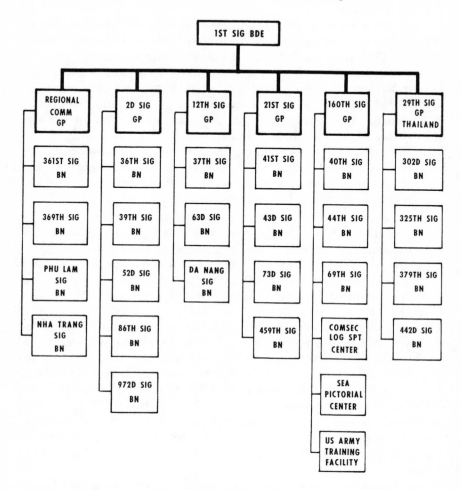

ational in December 1968, with its headquarters in Phu Bai. The group had responsibility for all area communications support in the I Corps Tactical Zone and assumed command of the 37th and 63d Signal Battalions. On 1 July 1969 this group was redesignated the 12th Signal Group, commanded by Colonel Albert B. Crawford. By then the 1st Signal Brigade, with its extensive communications responsibilities throughout Southeast Asia, comprised six signal groups and twenty-three battalions. (*Chart 2*)

In December 1968 there were scattered throughout the Republic of Vietnam approximately 220 installations for which the Corps Area System provided communications. To meet the requirements

MAP 6

of these large corps area communications facilities, ten signal battalions of the 1st Signal Brigade were deployed throughout the country. (*Map 6*) These battalions operated approximately 250 area communications links, carrying over four thousand voice channels, and an additional fifty interconnections, with approximately 800 voice channels, as part of the Defense Communications System in Vietnam. Besides multichannel radio, the area battalions operated and maintained 69 local telephone switchboards, 64 message centers, and 8 minor message relay centers to support all users within the four zones.

CHAPTER X

Special Communications Operations and Innovations

Mobile Riverine Force: An Unusual Test

In June 1967 General Westmoreland created a new, completely integrated command composed of a U.S. Army infantry brigade and a U.S. Navy task force. This Mobile Riverine Force was amphibious, operating entirely afloat; it was reminiscent of river forces used by the United States in the Civil War when the Union Army operated on the Mississippi, Cumberland, and other rivers. The force was complete, independent of fixed support bases, and with all of its normal fire support embarked or in tow. The great flexibility of the Mobile Riverine Force increased our ability to take the fight to the Viet Cong in previously inaccessible areas. The battleground was the mighty Mekong River and its delta.

The Mekong Delta is drained principally by four channels of the Mekong River as it flows southeastward from Cambodia to the sea. Some 1,000 miles of primary canals crisscross the area, and in between the canals lie thousands of square miles of rich rice lands. Few roads penetrate the delta. Towns and villages sit on the mud banks of canals and rivers, surrounded by rice paddies. Little of the land is more than ten feet above sea level. Although the Mekong Delta is among the world's richest lands for rice-growing, it is formidable ground for the infantry soldier on foot and his modern, but often heavy, supporting equipment.

The assault unit of the Mobile Riverine Force was the 2d Brigade of the U.S. Army's 9th Infantry Division, a brigade specially tailored for combat on the rivers and canals. Since the riverine battalions operated from ships and assault craft, the infantrymen's traditional jeeps and trucks were not used. Instead, a small flotilla of boats powered by outboard motors was made available for transportation. The supporting artillery was streamlined for operation aboard towed barges instead of in fixed fire support bases. The organic communications resources of the riverine brigade were essentially the same used by other infantry except that man-packed, portable voice radios were substituted for those radios mounted on jeeps and trucks.

The U.S. Navy complement of the Mobile Riverine Force manned a fleet of assault troop carriers, fire support ships called monitors, command and communications boats, repair and supply ships, medical craft, a barracks barge, and two self-propelled barracks ships. These naval craft were specially prepared and outfitted in the United States for deployment on the waters of the delta. They were rigged with extra guns and cannon and were heavily armor-plated to ward off the inevitable Viet Cong rocket-propelled grenades and heavy-caliber machine gun rounds.

The command and communications boat was, as the name suggests, a floating command post, providing radio communications for both the Army troop commander and the Navy boat commander. One of these craft was usually available for each battalion-size element in an operation. This communications boat itself took on the appearance of a floating antenna field, since nine combat voice radios were installed below the deck and the topside bristled with nine antennas. With this equipment the troop commander maintained radio contact with his assault troops, the supporting artillery located nearby on barges, the ever-present helicopter gunships circling overhead, the monitors—fire support boats—the tactical fighter bombers of the Air Force, the South Vietnamese Army counterpart commander, higher headquarters, and the medical evacuation helicopters.

Much of the credit for maintaining such extensive communications must go to the communicators of the Mobile Riverine Force, both Army and Navy, who eliminated the interference inherent in having so many radios transmitting and receiving from a floating metal platform. The successful operation of radio circuits from the command and communications boats can be attributed to excellent frequency control, many on-the-spot innovations, and a degree of divine providence.

The USS *Benewah,* one of the self-propelled barracks ships, was the command post of the entire Mobile Riverine Force and was the rear headquarters of the 9th Infantry Division's 2d Brigade, the Army complement. It was the job of the 9th Signal Battalion, the organic communications unit of the division, to provide and operate telephone and message communications between the USS *Benewah* and division headquarters. Methods were quickly devised to track, by means of radio, the USS *Benewah* while it sailed on the delta's canals and streams; by use of multichannel radio relay

USS BENEWAH, A RIVERINE FORCE COMMAND CONTROL FLAGSHIP

equipment, the essential telephone and message communications were maintained. Whenever the ship approached the maximum range limit of the radio equipment, relay stations were activated in strategic locations to span the miles and maintain solid communications. Initially, the directional antennas both at the ground stations and aboard the USS *Benewah* were kept properly aimed, as the ship sailed or swung at anchor, by signalmen turning the antennas slowly by hand until the strongest signal was indicated on the receivers. This effective but primitive system was soon replaced with special antenna-rotating motors rushed from the United States. The rotating motors were similar in design and were operated on the same principle as the "rotors" which many families have for their home TV antennas.

In June 1968 the 9th Signal Battalion was faced with the problem of establishing telephone and message communications for another floating command post besides that on the USS *Benewah*. This forward command post of the Mobile Riverine Force was operating from a medium landing craft only 73 feet long and 21 feet wide. Since the boat was far too small to accommodate the radios and power generators as well as the men of the forward command post, a second landing craft was found on which the 9th Signal Battalion troopers installed multichannel radio relay equipment and power generators.

The effectiveness of this system of communications can best be illustrated by describing a deployment of the Mobile Riverine

Force in December 1968. A multichannel radio link was installed from the 9th Infantry Division main command post at Dong Tam to the Mobile Riverine Force forward command post located in the My Tho River a few miles from Dong Tam. As this command post craft moved down the river in the early morning hours, destined for Vung Tau and its ultimate site in Long An Province, the USS *Benewah* also weighed anchor and sailed for Vung Tau. As each ship entered the South China Sea, the 9th Signal Battalion relay station at Vung Tau picked up each radio link and relayed it back to Dong Tam. The signalmen at Vung Tau were constantly rotating antennas for maximum signal strength, as were the signalmen aboard the USS *Benewah* and the forward command post vessel.

At Vung Tau the USS *Benewah* anchored, but the landing craft containing the forward command post and the waterborne radio relay equipment moved up various twisting canals and waterways to a position forty-five miles northwest of Vung Tau. This movement took several days. Each night the two landing craft beached and established a base from which supporting artillery fire was provided and controlled through the telephone circuits passing over the radio relay link. While the boats were moving, the Mobile Riverine Force forward command post, of course, had no access to these telephone circuits. But as soon as the boats either beached or anchored, the 2d Brigade's commander and his staff on the landing craft were provided with the telephone and message communications via field wire strung between the two vessels. Because of this increase in communications support, the Army and Navy commanders of the Mobile Riverine Force now had the capability to operate at distances far from their rear or permanent headquarters and still influence and control the over-all operation of the force.

The Mobile Riverine Force was a highly successful U.S. combat unit throughout its period of operation. The innovations of the 9th Infantry Division signalmen tied this potent amphibious force together by means of solid communications, while the force elements freely operated in waterways that were previously controlled, for the most part, by the Viet Cong.

Battlefield Secure Voice Equipment

One of the most significant and vital communications innovations during the Vietnam War was the development of equipment capable of providing complete security to the combat voice radio nets of the fighting units. From the early days of the war the senior commanders could discuss classified matters over fixed secure long-distance telephone systems such as "Talk Quick" and ultimately over the worldwide, sophisticated Automatic Secure Voice Communications System. But the division commander and his battalion commanders did not have the means of discussing classified operations with their combat units unless a message was written, encoded, and transmitted over either the voice radio net or the message circuits. The procedure was extremely slow and therefore suffered from the all too common practice of not being followed at all. The hope that "maybe the enemy is not listening this time" was much too prevalent in the U.S. forces. This false sense of security did not appear for the first time in the Vietnam War; it was equally common during World War II and the Korean War.

The Communists in Vietnam had always capitalized on their ability to mount a surprise attack with rockets or mortars or to plan an ambush with mines and machine gun fire. During 1968 there was growing evidence that the enemy was placing greater emphasis on exploiting our communications through interception and communications deception. As far back as the 1967 battle for Dak To, Viet Cong radios eavesdropped on U.S. radio transmissions. When fighter bombers asked the U.S. infantry to place yellow smoke in front of the most forward friendly positions, enemy mortars dropped yellow smoke on our troops, hoping to mislead the Air Force into bombing friendly forces.

During an operation in January 1968 near the Cambodian border, units of the U.S. Army's 25th Infantry Division were startled to hear a radio operator claiming to be the leader of an Australian patrol just ahead of them. The American commander, whose radio call sign was MANCHU SIX, was skeptical. His patrol started a search. As the U.S. troops were moving through the jungle, the unknown radio operator called "MANCHU SIX, MANCHU SIX, this is ALFA BRAVO 13, over." When the infantry commander replied, the alleged Australian station transmitted, ". . . the Viet Cong in my area are moving up on your southern flank, repeat, southern flank, over." When his troops deployed on the southern flank began to receive small arms fire, the U.S. battalion commander asked for an identification. The reply was "We are an Australian 173d Airborne unit and we were dropped here this morning at 0600 hours, approximately 23 meters north. We are on a search and destroy mission. Over." A careful check with the command operations centers of both the 25th Infantry Division and II Field Force revealed that the Australian forces did not have a unit with a "173" designation and that, further, there were no Australian forces operating in the immediate area at that time. The next radio transmission heard was "BRAVO BRAVO 15, this is ALFA BRAVO 13. The American unit just east of you, repeat, just east of you, thinks you're Victor Charlie [Viet Cong]. Do you read? Over." At that point the U.S. battalion commander got on his radio and advised the unknown stations that they should "stay on the ground and not move. If you do not move around, everything will be okay. If, in fact, you are phony and a VC station and continue to move to my location then I will consider you enemy forces and will engage. Do you roger? Over." The unknown station stated that it would stand off and not move until contacted by the U.S. infantrymen. But these allegedly friendly troops were never heard from again. A search of the area by U.S. troops revealed no Australians at all; in fact, the only signs of prior occupancy were abandoned ambush positions of the Viet Cong that showed signs of hasty departure.

These instances emphasized the magnitude of the Viet Cong and North Vietnamese efforts to intercept Allied communications.

The simplest and fastest method for intercept is, of course, to use captured communications equipment. By mid-1968, the Viet Cong and North Vietnamese had in their possession many American-made radios which they had captured, primarily the portable radios used by U.S. infantry soldiers.

However, the efforts of the Viet Cong and North Vietnamese to monitor U.S. radio transmissions in order to use the information against us were increasingly frustrated as secure voice equipment became available. The first such equipment received in Vietnam was developed for use with combat voice radios mounted on vehicles, and for sets placed in tactical operations centers and similar locations. This configuration, received in 1966, allowed the radio operators who worked from essentially fixed locations, such as division and brigade headquarters, to discuss classified information freely because the enemy simply could not understand them.

The next breakthrough was the introduction in Vietnam during 1968 of smaller, man-carried, secure voice equipment which allowed patrols and small units operating in the jungles to secure their radio nets. That same year a model specially configured for installation in aircraft, both helicopters and conventional fixed-wing airplanes, was sent to Vietnam. The stage was now set for most of the U.S. mobile combat radio stations to operate in the secure voice mode.

Initially, however, the new equipment was not generally used. There were three reasons for this delay. First, certain special cables and unique items were slow in being sent from the United States. Second, there were misconceptions about the security require- ments, the integrity of the system, and the operational value of the equipment. Third and probably most important, a secure retrans- mit capability was not available; radios using the secure equipment could not automatically relay transmissions. The first two prob- lems were handled quickly. Emphatic messages were rushed to the United States and got the needed auxiliary equipment moving on the way. Instruction from senior officers and teams of Signal Corps communicators demonstrating the equipment helped the combat soldiers to realize its value. But the third problem, the lack of re- transmission capability, had to wait until 1969 for solution simply because the equipment did not yet exist. Once research and devel- opment and the wheels of industry were running at high speed, the secure voice repeaters were quickly obtained and put to efficient use in Vietnam. Thus, in the latter part of the war, these secure voice devices were extensively used—a big step toward the ulimate goal of completely securing the Army's combat communications.

Airborne Radio Relay

The success which the skytroopers of the 1st Cavalry Division had with airborne radio relay in the famous Ia Drang valley cam- paign in 1965 paved the way for extending a commander's ability to control the action on the battlefield. As the action of the war turned toward the remote valleys and plateaus bordering Laos and Cambodia, the cost—in terms of committed troops, expected casualties, and airlifts—of seizing and holding high ground for radio relay installation appeared to be excessive, if not prohibitive. Recalling the previous success of the 1st Cavalry Division, commu- nications-electronics planners of the U.S. Army, Vietnam, opted for an airborne radio relay system that would connect the field com- mander's combat voice radios with his higher headquarters. The call went out to the Department of the Army, and in early 1968 four relay aircraft were equipped and sent to Vietnam. They were successfully tested in combat in February and soon were flying relay missions throughout the country. The airborne relays were particularly valuable in support of the 1st Cavalry Division's relief of Khe Sanh in the northern part of the I Corps Tactical Zone in the spring of 1968.

Although these airborne relays extended the field commander's span of control and often provided the only means of communica- ting with ground troops in contact with the enemy, there were ma- jor limitations to the system. These limitations primarily involved the aircraft itself. The twin-engine Caribou airplane that the 1st Cavalry Division employed so successfully in 1965 had subsequently been taken from the Army's inventory and turned over to the Air Force. As a result, the airborne radio relay system was installed in the Army's single-engine Otter airplane. These older Otters were difficult to maintain. The radios installed were not capable of secure voice retransmission and were actually too heavy for the underpowered Otter.

Once again, therefore, the Department of the Army was asked for help. U.S. Army, Vietnam, asked that the Otter be replaced with a more powerful, all-weather aircraft and that the present radios be replaced with newer, lighter models designed especially for aircraft. The result of this request was that the 1st Signal Brigade received nine twin-engine U–21, or "Ute," aircraft in the fall of 1969. Each was equipped with a radio console capable of relaying three voice radio nets. But the most significant fact was that all three nets could now operate and be relayed in the secure voice mode. The first missions involving this new relay system proved that a secure voice radio link of 140 nautical miles could be readily established at an altitude of only 3,500 feet. Since the Army's U–21 plane can stay aloft on station for several hours at a much higher altitude, the occasions when a small unit or long-range patrol was without communications were virtually nonexistent.

Airborne radio relay, however, contributed to the problem of radio frequency interference. The frequency spectrum for the combat radios was very limited and had to be allocated among the many U.S. Army and other combat units deployed in Vietnam. In order to minimize the interference of the radio nets with each other, judicious planning was necessary to assure that those units which had to share a common frequency were sufficiently separated. All of this careful planning was for naught, however, when an airborne relay station was capable of transmitting over five or six times the distance of a station on the ground. Invariably, reports of frequency interference would start to arrive at a combat headquarters shortly after the relay aircraft arrived in its assigned orbit. The only feasible solution was for the U.S. Army, Vietnam, to reserve a certain number of frequencies for use in airborne radio relay operations alone. This expedient solved the interference problem but further decreased the number of radio frequencies available for general use. Therefore detailed frequency management was essential from the maneuver battalion to the highest levels in Vietnam.

Pictorial Operations

The face of war is ugly, but it is a face that must be recorded. Recording and photographing the war was one of the missions of the U.S. Army Signal Corps in Vietnam.

A young lieutenant deploys his infantrymen into an ambush position to the accompaniment of the soft whir of a motion picture camera. Farther north a medical evacuation mission flying through heavy enemy fire is recorded in a series of short clicks drowned out by the roar of the helicopter. In the Mekong Delta, a U.S. Army unit helps build homes in a small village as one man with a necklace of cameras surveys the scene through a light meter. Unconnected? No, not really. To the Signal Corps combat photographer it is just another day of recording both the war itself and the Army's reconstruction efforts throughout South Vietnam.

In 1962 the only operational U.S. pictorial unit in Vietnam was an element of the 39th Signal Battalion. Late in 1965 this element was transferred to the 69th Signal Battalion, where it merged with the 69th's organic Audio-Visual Platoon. The capabilities of the resulting organization were generally limited to black and white still photography on a very modest scale. The arriving U.S. combat divisions and separate brigades had their own photographic sections, as did the signal battalions of the field forces, but their capability was also limited to a few combat photographers and black and white film production.

As the war increased in intensity, so did the clamor for photographic documentation. In order to place some control over the countrywide pictorial effort, the 1st Signal Brigade created the Southeast Asia Pictorial Agency late in 1966; however, this was only a staff or management type of agency, consisting of one or two officers. Not until almost a year later was there any significant improvement in photography and processing film.

In August 1967 the pictorial agency was redesignated the Southeast Asia Pictorial Center. Concurrently, men and equipment for photo support on a large scale began to arrive in Vietnam. This organization soon became the most extensive and complex photo facility the U.S. Army had ever placed in a combat zone. In addition to its central facilities at Long Binh, the pictorial center maintained and operated photo support units at Phu Bai, An Khe, Cam Ranh Bay, Can Tho, and Saigon. Each unit was capable of providing complete photographic service within its area of operation. The Southeast Asia Pictorial Center was the first Army photo facility to be capable of color processing and printing in a combat zone.

COMBAT PHOTOGRAPHER OF 221ST SIGNAL COMPANY GETS A HELPING HAND FROM VIETNAMESE CIVILIAN

The Southeast Asia Pictorial Center was operated by the 221st Signal Photographic Company. This unit, activated in June 1966 at Fort Monmouth, New Jersey, arrived in Vietnam in photographic team increments during 1967 and 1968 and has a short but colorful combat history. Its combat photographers as well as those of the organic signal units of the field forces, divisions, and bri-

COMMUNICATOR PLACES A MARS CALL, CHRISTMAS 1969

gades, captured on film the realities of the Vietnam War. Coura-
geously entering the combat area, armed with a roll of film and a
camera, photographers sometimes lost their lives as they tried to
capture the action of the combat men they accompanied. One of
these photographers was Specialist David A. Russell of the 221st
Signal Company, who was killed in action on 18 March 1969 while
on a combat photo mission in South Vietnam. The 1st Signal Brigade dedicated a new Army message relay center at Long Binh on
25 October 1970 and named it the Russell Army Relay.

Military Affiliate Radio System

The Military Affiliate Radio System, or MARS as it is popularly known, is a worldwide network of military and designated civilian ham, or amateur, radio stations. Its mission is to provide
emergency backup and supplemental radio links for U.S. Department of Defense communications. MARS operators perform vital

services for both the military and civilian population. Their services range from establishing rescue communications following an earthquake or tornado to allowing a combat soldier to talk via radio telephone to his wife.

The MARS operation in Vietnam is definitely small when compared with all other Army communication services provided, but to hundreds of thousands of servicemen in Vietnam and their families back home it has been the most important service provided by the Signal Corps. After receiving the approval of the government of the Republic of Vietnam, the Military Affiliate Radio System began operation in Vietnam in late 1965, with all U.S. armed services participating. The Army MARS program in Vietnam started with just six stations. A personal radio and telephone hookup, or "phone patch," service began in February 1966 when the Department of the Army authorized the Vietnam MARS stations to make contact with designated stations in the United States. A U.S. contact station would then place a collect telephone call to a designated home, and for five minutes a soldier in Vietnam, perhaps one just in from a jungle patrol, could talk to his folks, who were halfway around the world. True, the reception was not always good because of ionospheric storms and weather disturbances. But who cared when an amateur radio operator in the United States was relaying to a soldier on a remote fire base in Vietnam the message "yes, she loves you and yes, she will marry you, over."

The U.S. Army, Vietnam, portion of the MARS program was completed in October 1969 with a total of forty-seven MARS stations throughout the republic, operating in seven different nets. The number of contact stations in the United States had grown to over a hundred. In the spring of 1970 the number of phone patches, or completed connections, from Vietnam to the United States reached an all-time high, averaging over 42,000 each month. At the conclusion of the MARS expansion program in Vietnam, soldiers in every American unit had access to a local MARS station. The backbone of the MARS stations in Vietnam was a commercially purchased, "off-the-shelf," single sideband radio, which was capable of spanning great distances. It was not only the mainstay for the MARS stations, but also for several years was used constantly in Vietnam to meet combat requirements for a long-range radio.

CHAPTER XI

Sophistication of U.S. Army Communications in Vietnam

Whereas the years from 1962 to 1967 were devoted to building the communications foundation in Vietnam, 1968 and 1969 were years of completion and sophistication. During that period the huge Integrated Wideband Communications System was finished. The telephone and message networks in Vietnam were further integrated and consolidated. For the first time, modern automatic switching equipment for both voice and message traffic was introduced into a combat zone.

Completion of the Integrated Communications System

The final links of Phases I and II of the Integrated Wideband Communications System were completed in the first two months of 1968. Their completion marked a communications milestone, extending high quality, multichannel communications throughout Vietnam: north to Hue, south to major cities in the Mekong Delta, and westward into Thailand. The fact that these two phases of the wideband system were completed and cut to traffic at this time had extreme combat significance. Many critical mobile assets could now be relieved from their interim service in the long-lines system and could be transferred to the north in support of the heavy troop buildup and unit relocations within I Corps Tactical Zone. The *Tet* offensive and the massing of enemy troops in the Demilitarized Zone and in the area of the Khe Sanh combat base had led to the strengthening of I Corps Tactical Zone.

Construction and installation at the new sites of Phase III, the final phase of the integrated long-lines system, were underway at the outset of 1968 and continued through the perilous weeks of the *Tet* offensive. Work on the new Phase III links and on system improvements progressed steadily, and by the end of the year all but one of the twenty-six links and upgrades had been completed and put into service. The uncompleted link was between Qui Nhon and Nha Trang.

". . . *HOLD YER HATS FELLAS . . .*
HERE COMES ANOTHER ONE OF THE SIGNAL BRIGADE'S
'MODERN, SOPHISTICATED COMMUNICATIONS SYSTEMS'. . ."

This last link of Phase III was accepted and put to traffic in January 1969. After four and a half years of effort and at a cost of approximately $235 million, the most massive undertaking in the history of the Army Signal Corps was finally finished, constituting throughout South Vietnam and Thailand the fixed-station, commercial-quality Integrated Wideband Communications System. (*Map 7*)

One final addition to the civilian contract for the wideband system was awarded in March 1968 for the provision and installation of four transportable, line-of-sight, microwave terminals. These transportable facilities had all the technical control capabilities and high channel capacity of the fixed wideband stations, plus the very distinct advantage that they could be moved if needed elsewhere. The first of these microwave terminals to be put into full operation was at Dong Ha, just a few kilometers south of the Demilitarized Zone. On 20 April 1969 this terminal linked with the fixed-station terminal at Quang Tri. Work was continuing, meanwhile, on the three other transportable facilities being installed at Di An, a few miles north of Saigon, at Sa Dec, in the delta, and at Dong Ba Thin, near Cam Ranh Bay. All these facilities were operational by July 1969.

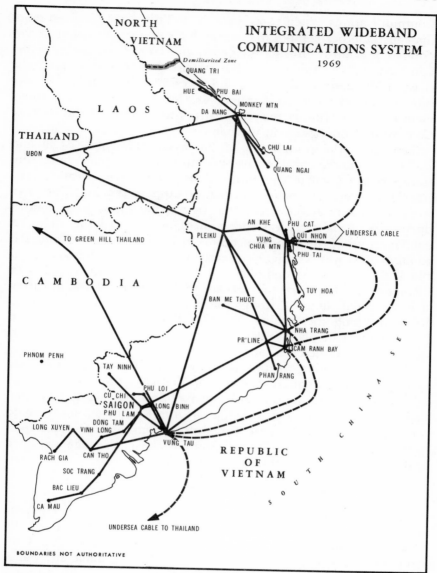

MAP 7

Integration of Defense Communications

In November 1968, the Department of Defense redesignated its telecommunications systems in Southeast Asia as the Integrated

Communications System, Southeast Asia. This move involved more than just another complicated name. Now one single system incorporated previously distinct elements: the large fixed-station wideband system, the undersea cable system that looped around the coast of Vietnam to Thailand, and a considerable number of mobile line-of-sight and tropospheric scatter radio facilities, supplementing and extending the terminal points, or tails, of the Defense Communications System in Vietnam.

Soon after the completion of the fixed wideband system and the establishment of the over-all integrated system, numerous transportable combat communications links were released, and, since they were no longer needed to support the long-lines network, they were at once relocated to provide support for combat operations. A most critical and immediate need was the major reconfiguration of the communications in I Corps Tactical Zone. Reconfiguration was completed in early January 1969, thereby releasing U.S. Air Force tropospheric scatter systems, which had been "temporarily" deployed to Vietnam in 1966 when it was apparent that the rapid influx of troops was surpassing the limited capability of the long-lines system. The Air Force equipment, however, had remained in place and in use for three years, until the backbone system attained full capacity in 1969.

Similar "purging" of the integrated long-lines system was soon accomplished throughout the rest of Vietnam; the result was the release of considerable quantities of mobile signal equipment that had been previously committed, as an interim stopgap measure, to the support of the Defense Communications System. The Integrated Communications System, Southeast Asia, became stable in mid-1969, thus yielding the fruit of much labor.

Automatic Message Switching—Another First

The activation of automatic message and data switching centers at Phu Lam and Nha Trang in early 1968 introduced the worldwide Automatic Digital Network into Vietnam. The Phu Lam switching center of this network began passing traffic in March 1968. The flow of traffic through the Phu Lam switching center wrote a new chapter in communications history: the multimillion dollar switch was the first of its kind ever to be installed in a combat zone in sight of Viet Cong patrols. A similar automatic switch was activated at Nha Trang on 3 June 1968. Subscriber message terminals to serve the U.S. forces were activated as fast as the equipment was available. At the end of 1968, the Phu Lam switch was serving twenty-eight subscriber terminals with an average daily

CHECKING A CONSOLE AT PHU LAM AUTOMATIC MESSAGE SWITCHING CENTER. *White rubber-soled shoes were required in dust-free, temperature-controlled building necessary for equipment.*

traffic volume of 37,000 messages. Nha Trang, serving nineteen subscribers, was handling more than 25,000 messages daily.

The 1st Signal Brigade was charged with the responsibility of operating and maintaining not only the two automatic switching centers based in Vietnam, but also all Army subscriber terminals that were connected to the big automatic switches. The digital network provided the primary trunking for the Defense Department's integrated automatic and nonautomatic message network in Vietnam. At its peak, the system handled in excess of 100,000 messages per day, with the Army portion of the network encompassing some eighty-six communications centers with twenty-five automatic digital terminals. Within this count were the automatic terminals provided to the combat divisions throughout the country. From Camp Eagle in the north, near the city of Hue, home of the 101st Airborne Division, to Cu Chi in III Corps Tactical Zone, home of the 25th Infantry Division, communicators from the 1st Signal Brigade operated low-speed, 100-words-per-minute automatic terminals. Usually mounted on vans but sometimes installed in a fixed facility, these terminals provided the division commander with direct worldwide access for message communications.

In only two years, from the activation of the Phu Lam automatic switching center in 1968 to late 1970, the automatic message system in Vietnam expanded to meet the requirements of centralized control and accurate, high-speed communications. The impact of the Automatic Digital Network on record communications in a war zone was immense because for the first time U.S. forces possessed a reliable and accurate high-speed method of ordering ammunition and repair parts, reporting casualties, and requesting replacements.

In late 1969 some of the last necessary refinements were made on the message communications system in Vietnam. The older manual message relay facilities at Phu Lam and Da Nang were phased out of service. The Nha Trang relay had been relegated to the less important role of minor relay in December 1968. These relays had carried the burden of message communications in Vietnam and served as the gateway stations to the rest of the world since the early 1960s. But manual tape relays proved to be too slow for our modern army in combat. The inevitable arrival of automatic switching in the combat zone marked the end of an era in military communications, the end of the reliance on torn-tape relay as the basis for message communications, and another step in our progress to writer-to-reader secure communications.

Tandem Switches—An Ultimate

At the end of 1968 the Southeast Asia Automatic Telephone Service was nearing completion, and the many years of operator-assisted long-distance telephone calls were coming to an end. In November of that year the first automatic long-distance telephone switching center at Bang Pla, near Bangkok, Thailand, was completed and cut over to service. The remaining switching centers in Vietnam and Thailand were in various stages of completion. On 22 February 1969 the Can Tho automatic switch was completed. Its cutover was followed by cutovers of centers at Korat, Thailand, in March, and at Da Nang in mid-April 1969. The telephone switching centers at Tan Son Nhut and Nha Trang were completed at the end of July. Installation continued at the centers of the remaining sites at Pleiku, Vung Chua Mountain near Qui Nhon, and Ubon, Thailand. These last three switches became operational by the end of 1969, thus completing the long-distance direct dial system for Southeast Asia.

The nine switches comprising this system were connected to some fifty-four automatic dial telephone exchanges of the Army, Navy, and Air Force in Vietnam and Thailand, allowing selected subscribers and all dial telephone exchange operators to dial directly any telephone subscriber in Southeast Asia, and giving access into the worldwide Automatic Voice Network. The U.S. automatic dial telephone exchanges in Vietnam, which had access to the long-distance system, were by themselves processing over 1,000,000 telephone calls each day in 1969. (Map 8)

Another critical and essential long-distance telephone service was in the area of command control. In the summer of 1967 the 1st Signal Brigade installed small automatic telephone exchanges, dubbed "emergency action consoles," at the command operations centers of the U.S. Military Assistance Command in Saigon and of U.S. Army, Vietnam, at Long Binh. These consoles provided automatic telephone service to the essential subscribers in Saigon and Long Binh. In addition, the control elements of the subordinate commands, down to separate brigade levels, were connected to both emergency action consoles by separate long-distance telephone circuits.

The Signal Soldier

The growth of U.S. and Free World Military Assistance Forces in the Republic of Vietnam from 1962 to 1968 brought with it problems concerning the personnel needed to operate and main-

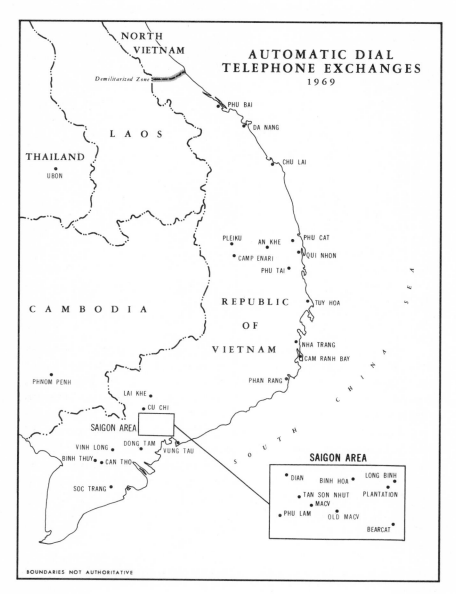

MAP 8

tain the widespread communications facilities. The problems came from many sources, among them the lack of certain select specialists and the introduction of new equipment into Vietnam when the operators had no previous training in the United States. Although assigned strengths lagged behind authorized figures throughout the entire U.S. Army in Vietnam, I will discuss here only those manpower problems that were peculiar to the U.S. Army Signal Corps operating in Vietnam and the actions that were taken to ease these problems.

Operation and maintenance difficulties often arose when new equipment was introduced into Vietnam before the Army's schools in the United States could provide trained men. This situation forced the operating signal units to take soldiers away from their primary and essential duties and either give them on-the-job training with the new equipment or send them to the 1st Signal Brigade's Army Training Facility at Long Binh for formal instruction. Typical examples of such equipment were the commercial dial switching gear of the telephone network and the data transmission terminals associated with the Automatic Digital Network.

One of the most critical manpower shortages was in the specialty of communications cable-splicer. Long before the communications expansion in Vietnam, the decision had been made by the U.S. Army to discontinue cable-splicing as a course of instruction and instead to send Army students to the joint course conducted by the Air Force at Sheppard Air Force Base in Texas. As heavy cable construction became routine in all of the large Vietnam base camps, it was apparent that the numbers graduating from this joint course could not meet the requirements of the U.S. Army, Vietnam, for trained splicers. The shortage was largely alleviated by introducing a cable-splicing course at the 1st Signal Brigade's Army Training Facility in Vietnam. While this method produced a journeyman-soldier capable of beginning work on heavy cable construction projects and making repairs, the time he spent at the school decreased the time left in the soldier's 12-month tour in which his new-found skills could be put to use. We also had difficulties in other fields. Many microwave, tropospheric scatter, radar, computer, and cryptographic specialists arriving in Vietnam needed additional training before they could perform their tasks in an acceptable manner. These men were given refresher courses at the brigade's training facility.

Another area of concern was that signal personnel arrived in Vietnam from two different sources. Signal officers and men for the 1st Signal Brigade were requisitioned through channels of the Strategic Communications Command from the Department of the Army. Men for the signal units of the field forces, divisions, and

CABLE-SPLICERS AT WORK AT A LARGE FIXED BASE

separate brigades were requisitioned through U.S. Army, Vietnam, from the Department of the Army. Of necessity, requisitions were submitted many months in advance of the arrival of the replacements, and often the requirement for an individual with a particular specialty in a specific unit had been satisfied by other means prior to his arrival in Vietnam. In order to utilize replacements most effectively and retain the flexibility necessary to respond to the changing requirements, a weekly meeting was established in 1968 between the 1st Signal Brigade and the communications-electronics staff of the U.S. Army, Vietnam, to discuss the personnel situation. Decisions were then made to divert incoming manpower resources or to reassign men already in Vietnam to meet urgent requirements. Through this procedure the possible detriment of the dual replacement stream was avoided, and an effective method emerged for using signal officers and enlisted men arriving in Vietnam.

Supply and Maintenance Support

The communications equipment used in Vietnam ranged in size and complexity from large, fixed-plant items to the squad radio used by the infantry soldier. All this equipment required an efficient repair and supply system in order to insure continuing communications. The procedures for providing this support differed between the mobile and fixed communications items and these differences ultimately led to problems.

An appreciation of the difficulties inherent in communications supply support can be gained by an examination of the sheer magnitude of the communications-electronics logistics effort at the height of the Vietnam War. An estimated one-third of all the major items of equipment in Vietnam were communications-electronics items. Over 50,000 different types of communications-electronics replacement and repair parts were stocked by the supply system in Vietnam. And there were more than 150 direct and general support supply and maintenance facilities in Vietnam that dealt with communications-electronics equipment.

The supply and maintenance support for the communications equipment of the combat units and of the corps area support battalions under the 1st Signal Brigade was standardized, following the guidelines of the Army's logistics doctrine. This support functioned as effectively as the over-all Army logistics system in Vietnam functioned. When the U.S. forces began to arrive in strength, the huge logistical buildup created unprecedented problems which the Army had to solve in order to fight a computerized war in the counterinsurgency combat environment of Vietnam. However, in time the depot and support command system of management functioned well, and the computer as a tool of logistic management came of age in Vietnam.

The standardization that was possible for mobile communications-electronics equipment was not feasible for the fixed-plant communications equipment used in Vietnam. Our fixed signal equipment in Southeast Asia was mainly a combination of commercial equipment provided by and partly or wholly maintained by two commercial contractors. Such equipment was new to the Army and involved uncommon components that were not found at all in the field army maintenance support system. These items, therefore, presented unprecedented problems for the logistician in the matter of the availability of repair parts, the application of standard Army maintenance doctrine, and the training of military technicians to maintain the equipment.

CALIBRATING EQUIPMENT AT 1ST SIGNAL BRIGADE CAN THO SITE

The problems were apparent to both the logistician and the communicator alike. During the summer of 1968 a Department of the Army team, headed by Brigadier General Hugh F. Foster, Jr., prepared a study of communications-electronics support in Southeast Asia. The study defined the logistics concepts and the support responsibilities for the fixed communications systems in Southeast Asia. Specifically, it recommended that three area maintenance and supply facilities be established, two in Vietnam and one in Thailand. These facilities, to be operated solely by and for the 1st Signal Brigade, were to furnish the maintenance and supply support for the commercially procured, fixed-plant communications equipment in Southeast Asia.

In October 1968 approval of the recommendation came from the Department of the Army, and construction of facilities at Bangkok, Thailand, and at Long Binh, Vietnam, was begun promptly. The Thailand complex, under the 29th Signal Group, became operational in June 1969, and the Long Binh facility followed a month later. Shortly thereafter, construction was started on the third facility at Cam Ranh Bay, which became operational in the spring of 1970.

The activation of these area maintenance and supply facilities solved one of the major problems in the support of fixed communications systems. These systems, previously supported by contracts and ill-defined maintenance and supply channels, were now supported from a single central facility in each of the three designated geographical areas of responsibility.

CHAPTER XII

Vietnamization and Related Activities

Background

In the wake of the 1968 *Tet* offensive, major decisions were made affecting the course of the war in Vietnam. By the end of that year the Paris peace talks had begun and the United States had halted the bombing of North Vietnam. Upon the advent of the Nixon administration a major shift occurred in U.S. foreign policy, as announced by the President at Guam in July 1969. In an address on 3 November 1969, President Richard M. Nixon declared that the United States would provide economic and military assistance in accordance with U.S. treaty commitments, and stated: "We shall look to the nation directly threatened to assume the primary responsibility of providing the manpower for its defense."

The United States would continue to seek peace in Vietnam through negotiation. If that method did not succeed, the United States would, as an alternative, strengthen the South Vietnamese armed forces so that they could take over the responsibilities of defending their nation. The "alternative," a plan called Vietnamization, was initiated after Secretary of Defense Melvin R. Laird's trip to Vietnam in March 1969. It provided for redeployment of U.S. troops on a programmed basis, as the South Vietnamese armed forces became more self-sufficient.

The U.S. troop withdrawals would be accomplished in phases. The first phase, the withdrawal of 25,000 men, announced in June 1969, included elements of the U.S. Army's 9th Infantry Division and a U.S. Marine regiment. Over the next eighteen months withdrawal figures grew, so that U.S. strength, which had stood at about 535,000 at the start of 1969 declined to about 335,000 by the end of 1970, with major deployments planned for the near future.

Communications Vietnamization: The Plan

Implementing the Vietnamization program required a plan for a communications system to satisfy the diminishing U.S. requirements and to meet the long-range needs of the Vietnamese government and its armed forces. Plans were developed by the U.S. Military Assistance Command in the fall of 1969 for a time-phased turnover to the Republic of Vietnam of a backbone system to meet the needs both of the South Vietnamese and of the remaining U.S. and other Free World Military Assistance Forces. A U.S. Army communications planning group, which was formed from U.S. Army, Vietnam, and 1st Signal Brigade staffs, made recommendations to the U.S. Military Assistance Command, Vietnam, in the form of a "strawman" plan.

The plan required that portions of the fixed Integrated Communications System and the Corps Area Communications System be turned over to the South Vietnamese. Selected terminal equipment, such as fixed automatic dial telephone exchanges and manual telephone switchboards with their associated cable systems, also would be turned over where required. The considerable residue of U.S. communications equipment would be withdrawn from Vietnam. On a long-range basis the U.S. communications assets remaining in Vietnam would be capable of consolidation into a single integrated telecommunications system, to be operated by the government of Vietnam. To achieve the Vietnamization of the complex communications system, of course, skilled Vietnamese operators, maintenancemen, and managers were necessary. The training of Vietnamese communicators now became a matter of highest priority.

Training the South Vietnamese Signalmen

Since 1961 South Vietnam had been training its own signalmen at the Signal School of the Republic of Vietnam Armed Forces at Vung Tau. This school had primarily concerned itself with providing Vietnamese signal personnel to operate and maintain combat communications systems. In line with the Vietnamization program, the school had increased its student capacity until it reached 2,500 by August of 1969. However, the South Vietnamese signal school was not capable of training its signalmen in the so-called hard, or higher, skills required to operate the Integrated Communications System, Southeast Asia, and the automatic dial telephone exchanges. As a result, U.S. Army, Vietnam, was asked to provide the necessary training.

For this task, the 1st Signal Brigade was well suited. The brigade, with its responsibilities for the operation and maintenance of the extensive communications system which would be turned over to the Vietnamese, already possessed soldier-experts. These experts were readily available and would work with the South Vietnamese during the conversion period. Such co-operation, however, was

GENERAL FOSTER OBSERVING VIETNAMESE SIGNAL TRAINING CLASS

nothing new. The signalmen of the brigade had been working for years with their Vietnamese counterparts through the "Buddy System," a program initiated in July 1966 by General Terry in coordination with the Vietnamese Chief Signal Officer. It had three major objectives: to improve the training of the South Vietnamese signalmen, to support civic action projects which would be beneficial to dependents of Vietnamese Signal Corps personnel, and to foster a closer relationship between the signalmen of both countries. By the end of 1969 twenty-five brigade units were actively participating in the program, then called Buddies Together, later called in Vietnamese *Cung Than Thien*.

By late 1969 the brigade had also begun formal training for the necessary Vietnamese hard-skill signal personnel at facilities provided by the Vietnamese signal school at Vung Tau. On 1 July

1970, shortly after I had left Vietnam and Major General Hugh F. Foster, Jr., had assumed the duties of Commanding General, 1st Signal Brigade, and Assistant Chief of Staff for Communications-Electronics, U.S. Army, Vietnam, a new signal training annex was put into operation near the Vietnamese signal school at Vung Tau. This contractor-operated facility, at which the hard-skill personnel would be trained, could accommodate 320 signal students.

The program to teach hard skills was in three phases. First, the South Vietnamese were taught to speak and read English at the South Vietnamese Armed Forces Language School. An understanding of English was necessary since the system would be used jointly by the United States and South Vietnam before it was turned over completely to South Vietnam. The language problem has been present throughout our experience in Vietnam and has never been really solved. Upon completion of this phase, the Vietnamese underwent formal training in one of the required skills of microwave radio repair, fixed-plant carrier repair, fixed-station technical control, or dial telephone exchange repair. After this formal training the Vietnamese signalmen were assigned to communications sites to work and learn on the job as apprentices for a little over six months. Once their training was completed, these Vietnamese signalmen augmented, and will eventually replace, U.S. military or contractor personnel at designated communications facilities. In addition to learning hard skills at Vung Tau, Vietnamese soldiers were being trained in the relatively simple soft skills, such as cable-splicing, communications line repair, and radio repair at the U.S. Army Training Facility which the 1st Signal Brigade operated at Long Binh.

Contractor Operation of Communications

In line with the Vietnamization program and the phased withdrawal of U.S. troops, the U.S. Army, Vietnam, developed a plan for contractor operation and maintenance of the Integrated Communications System, the dial telephone exchanges, and the two associated Army Signal maintenance and supply facilities in Vietnam. The plan, which had been approved in early 1970 by its enthusiastic advocate, Stanley R. Resor, Secretary of the Army, was known as COMVETS, Contractor Operation and Maintenance, Vietnam, Engineering and Training Services. A similar arrangement, COMTETS, was developed and ultimately approved for Thailand. In line with COMVETS, a contract was awarded toward the end of 1970 to the Federal Electric Corporation, a subsidiary of International Telephone and Telegraph, for the operation and

VIETNAM ARMY SIGNALMAN TRAINS ON THE JOB *at the first integrated communications site turned over to Vietnamese forces.*

maintenance of the fixed communications facilities. The contract also called for Federal Electric to provide future communications engineering maintenance and supply support in Vietnam.

Signal Troop Redeployments

As U.S. troops began to phase out of South Vietnam, the U.S. Army Signalmen who had been providing military communications support in the country, also began to redeploy. Some U.S. Army signal units were inactivated in South Vietnam itself, while other units were redeployed to the United States. In some cases, strengths and equipment authorizations were reduced by the reorganization of the units themselves. For example, the headquarters of the 972d Signal Battalion was inactivated in Vietnam during November 1969. The battalion's mission, that of providing contingency communications support throughout the Republic of Vietnam, was divided among the 2d, 12th, and 21st Signal Groups. Its companies, depending on essential needs, were either inactivated or assigned to other battalions. When the U.S. Army's 1st Infantry

Division redeployed to Fort Riley, Kansas, during the spring of 1970, the division's organic 121st Signal Battalion went with the division. As a result of the redeployment of the 1st Infantry Division's 1st Brigade from its base camp at Lai Khe, about forty spaces were deleted from the 1st Signal Brigade's 587th Signal Company, which had provided the base camp support to this combat division.

Recovery of Communications Assets

As the redeployment of U.S. forces progressed, selected communications equipment, not programmed for turnover to the government of South Vietnam and no longer required for our troops, became available for use outside of Vietnam. Combat equipment was either deployed with its unit or was turned back into the U.S. Army supply system for redistribution. Redistribution presented no major problem since mobile combat equipment is generally sturdy and is packaged so that it can be moved or stored without damaging it when handled according to standard procedures.

The recovery of fixed equipment, however, was another matter. This equipment had been shipped to Vietnam in bits and pieces, where it had been assembled and installed in the form of large communications facilities, for the most part in air-conditioned buildings. If the expensive fixed equipment was to be reused, there were problems in identifications, inventory, and packaging.

In early 1969 we organized an element in the 1st Signal Brigade specifically for the purpose of the recovery and redistribution of fixed equipment. This small group of men was charged with the task of dismantling, preserving, and packaging the equipment at locations in both Vietnam and Thailand. For example, during April 1970 two dial exchanges were recovered, one from Camp Enari in South Vietnam and one from Sattahip, south of Bangkok, in Thailand. Communications-electronics equipment from two other sites in Thailand were also recovered.

Reorganization of the 1st Signal Brigade

While U.S. troops were being phased out of Vietnam, the 1st Signal Brigade underwent a major reorganization on 1 March 1970. Involving some eighty-five units of the brigade, this reorganization was based on a plan which had been approved by the Department of the Army in 1968 and which was in accord with the Army's evolving communications position in South Vietnam. Many of the brigade's organizations that had been structured to operate mobile facilities were in fact operating numerous other facilities, such as fixed automatic dial telephone exchanges and message centers and relays on mountaintops. In addition, many attachments had been made in order to provide the specific resources required for a given mission. As a result, one battalion often controlled companies from several other battalions. This situation produced command, administrative, and morale problems. The 1970 reorganization of the 1st Signal Brigade was both an improvement and a reduction. Some battalion-size units, such as the 69th Signal Battalion, operated the fixed facilities. These units were reorganized and redesignated signal support agencies, according to the U.S. Army's policy of not designating units which operate fixed installations as battalions. Although not a part of the Vietnamization program, this reorganization resulted in a reduction of the number of men needed in the 1st Signal Brigade. By the end of 1970 the 1st Brigade's strength was approximately 14,000 officers and men, of which about 12,000 were in the Republic of Vietnam and about 2,000 with the brigade's 29th Signal Group in Thailand.

Communications Support in Cambodia, April–June 1970

Even as U.S. troops were being phased out, a major test of the flexibility of our communications systems in South Vietnam occurred when U.S. and South Vietnam forces sought to wipe out Communist sanctuaries in Cambodia during April–June 1970. A number of major operations were undertaken from Vietnam against these sanctuaries which Hanoi had for years used with impunity to stage and launch attacks into South Vietnam, Laos, and Thailand.

As the assault forces moved into Cambodia, the U.S. Army shifted its communications forward. The 1st Cavalry Division and the 4th and 25th Infantry Divisions established division forward command posts. The II Field Force set up a forward command post in the III Corps Tactical Zone near the Cambodian border at Go Dau Ha, thirty-five miles northwest of Saigon. As the combat situation changed, this command post was later moved to the vicinity of Tay Ninh City.

During the initial stages of the operation, communications between the maneuver elements and their base areas were provided by the combat units' organic man-packed and vehicle-mounted voice radios. As the attacking forces moved further into Cambodia, airborne and ground radio relays were used to extend the range of these radios. For example, the U.S. Army's 11th Armored Cavalry

Skytroop Communicators in Cambodia in Early 1970

Regiment maintained voice radio communications over long distances through a voice retransmission station located at the isolated radio relay site atop Nui Ba Den near Tay Ninh. Wherever possible, lightweight secure voice equipment was used with these radios to counter the enemy's communications intelligence. In addition, the combat communicators used mobile radios of longer range to provide voice and secure message links from the battle area to the division and field force command posts within Vietnam.

As the scale of the Cambodian operations broadened, the organic combat communications, including the multichannel assets of the attacking units, were moved forward. At the same time, requirements for command and control and for intelligence, logistics, and administrative circuits reaching into the forward areas mushroomed. The mobile assets of the 1st Signal Brigade were quickly deployed to replace the combat signal units as they moved their equipment into Cambodia with the attacking forces. Circuits were speedily activated over the brigade's extended Corps Area Communications System, providing the commanders of the top echelons in Vietnam with ready access to their force commanders in Cambodia. The signal brigade also provided extensive communications support to U.S. advisers who accompanied the attacking South Vietnamese armed forces, including secure message facilities and manual telephone switching service.

Once again U.S. Army communications, whether operated by a signalman with his small back-pack radio or a fixed communicator with his tropospheric scatter equipment, met the test and justified the statement made by General Abrams in February 1969 when he was speaking of communications in Vietnam to an assembly of key personnel in the III Corps Tactical Zone:

> What we have here in this country is a communications system that permits us to move our power from one end of the land to the other any time we want to. To move our air power, to change the focus of the B–52's, change our troop dispositions, change the flow of logistics to put it where it is the most needed . . . . The only way you can do all those things—and do them when you want—is with a good, sound communications system.

Summary, 1968–1970

During 1968 and 1970 our signalmen in Southeast Asia completed the U.S. Army's communications system. They wrapped up all the plans and projects, perfected the big networks together with their specialized voice and message switches, and provided quality communications for all users. They made such refinements as se-

ARMORED PERSONNEL CARRIERS OF THE 9TH DIVISION IN CAMBODIA. *Note vertical antennas for mobile radios.*

cure communications, priorities for key commanders, and direct distance dialing—all capable of being extended into primitive areas wherever sudden combat needs might arise. Our signalmen, while installing and operating all these systems, proved themselves to be good combat soldiers whenever the military situation placed them in the midst of firefights.

With the over-all communications-electronics job accomplished, our signal organizations were able to improve on other missions, for example, the Army's cryptographic support, the Army's photographic audio-visual capability, and the specialized maintenance and support facilities required daily by the equipment of the big backbone communications networks. But above all, this was a time of preparation for turning over the great communications systems that had been built up in the Republic of Vietnam to the Vietnamese people to operate and maintain as their own.

As the present study is being written, the South Vietnamese, with U.S. assistance, are preparing for the day when they will take over the operation of all communications-electronics in their homeland; this preparation goes on in the face of continued aggression directed by Hanoi. As the South Vietnamese grow in strength, U.S. soldiers are being withdrawn. Even as the redeployment occurs, U.S. Army Signal combat communicators are on the job providing communications for the U.S. Army's infantry, armor, artillery, and aviation; for engineers, medics, military police, logisticians, and intelligence personnel; for the U.S. Air Force and Navy; for the Free World Military Assistance Forces of Australia, Korea, New Zealand, and Thailand, and for the government of South Vietnam and its armed forces; for U.S. headquarters; for the advisers to the Vietnamese; and for U.S. civilian agencies in the Department of State and the U.S. Agency for International Development. During the years 1962 through 1970, approximately 120,000 U.S. Army Signalmen have served in South Vietnam and other countries of Southeast Asia.

CHAPTER XIII

Conclusions and Lessons Learned

The magnitude of Army communications in the war in Vietnam has exceeded the scale of their employment in any previous war in history. These communications have increased in the same proportion as has the extraordinary mobility of troops and of firepower, often delivered from aloft, whether by Army helicopter gunships, Air Force bombers and fighters, or Navy and Marine jet aircraft. In fact, the mobility and firepower of our Army would themselves have been unmanageable without the hitherto unheard-of mobile and fixed combat communications facilities and the skilled communicators that have evolved in this conflict.

As a professional soldier and communicator, I have developed my own conclusions and feel we have learned certain lessons concerning the Army's communications-electronics during the Vietnam War. The more important of these have been set down here, along with some ideas of what must be done in the future.

Control and Organization of Communications

The elimination of the fragmentation of control over the Army's communications-electronics efforts during the early stages of the buildup in late 1965 and early 1966 was most important in the provision of an effective and efficient communications service for the numerous and diverse customers in South Vietnam and other parts of Southeast Asia. This was accomplished by the marriage of elements of the Army's Strategic Communications Command, with its highly qualified personnel, capable of engineering, installing, and operating large fixed communications systems, and the combat theater signal troops, at that time consisting of the 2d Signal Group with its highly flexible mobility. From this marriage emerged the 1st Signal Brigade, a part of the United States Army Strategic Communications Command's global organization, but operationally under control of the United States Army, Vietnam, the Army component command in the Republic of Vietnam. Our Vietnamese experience, incidentally, has firmly convinced me that this worldwide organization must be more properly named the "U.S. Army Communications Command."

The 1st Signal Brigade operated the relatively fixed assets of the Defense Communications System. At the same time it had a highly mobile surge capabilty, that is, on short notice it could pour equipment and men into its Corps Area System in response to the needs of the commanders in each of the four corps tactical zones. The brigade's Corps Area signal groups also provided the base camp communications services in their tactical zones.

The last and of course a vital element in over-all communications support was the Combat Systems operated by the organic signal companies of the separate brigades and by the organic signal battalions of the divisions and corps-equivalent field forces. A basic decision for the control and direction of these systems was made simultaneously with the organization of the 1st Signal Brigade. This was the "dual-hatting" of one individual, a general officer, to serve as both the brigade commander and the U.S. Army, Vietnam, communications-electronics staff officer.

Such was the situation when I arrived in Vietnam in 1968. Wearing the staff hat, I could project Army-wide policy and guidance to both the combat signal elements with the fighting troops and the 1st Signal Brigade. Wearing the 1st Signal Brigade command hat and using the brigade's diversified capabilities, I could weld the entire Army communications-electronics effort into a harmonious whole. There is no doubt in my mind that "dual-hatting" allows for the best direction up and down the line through one individual, and is the way to assure effective command, control, and direction of the U.S. Army's communications-electronics.

Our signal organizational structure in Vietnam is sound and will serve as a model for the Army's future war zone communications structure. The major elements of the structure are the mobile Combat Systems, the Corps Area Communications System serving the theater of operations, and the Defense Communications System.

The mobile Combat Systems should continue to be provided by signal units organic in a division, a corps, and a field army. Our division signal battalion organizations in Vietnam are sound, as is the dual-hat arrangement in the division wherein the division's signal staff officer serves also as the division's signal battalion commander. At the Army corps level the present, relatively large, corps-type signal battalion, which in all cases in Vietnam has needed significant additional resources attached, should be reorganized into at least two battalions under a group headquarters. The

Corps Signal Group comander should wear two hats, serving concurrently as Corps Signal Officer. Communications support for field armies should also be provided by organic, highly mobile, and flexible signal organizations. In order to provide diversified mobile support to our field army, this organization must consist of more than one group under a signal brigade, with the commander also serving on the Army staff.

Behind these combat communication elements there should be a single organization to operate the Defense Communications System within and from the theater of operations and to provide at the same time a flexible, mobile, surge capability in support of the combat forces. Further, there should be a separate theater area system much like the system we have logically dubbed "Corps Area" in Vietnam. In a large theater this organization would be a command, consisting of several brigades. The commander of such an organization should also wear two hats. The organization must include skilled communications systems managers and be capable of engineering and installing major systems. It should be the point of contact with contractors and should directly manage all communications-electronics contracts. It should provide for the rehabilitation and operation of any existing commercial systems, and establish in the theater any required signal training facilities. In summary, the organization should be the focal point in communications expertise, providing and operating the Defense Communications System, operating a flexible area system, and providing a reserve throughout the theater of operations. Finally, I believe focalization of the diverse pieces which make up a viable communications-electronics system is a must at the General Staff level of the Department of the Army.

The Integrated System

To the man of business, time is money. To the professional soldier, time is lives. The time required to provide the high quality fixed communications system in Vietnam was too long. Fortunately, because we could use available mobile equipment of lower capacity and lower quality that had been employed during the years of readying the fixed system, communications-electronics did not fail the soldier in battle. But I believe that in the future we can do better by planning and programming for modularized high quality and high-capacity fixed and mobile long-lines systems that include the associated voice, message, and data traffic switches and terminals.

Completely modularized systems should be shipped as a package, to be assembled on the site. I refer to a complete system with groupings of equipment that can go on a mountaintop, including the shelters or buildings for the equipment, the air-conditioning and power units, the antennas, the compatible cryptographic equipment, the test equipment, the repair and maintenance gear, the housing for the contractors and soldiers who will install them and the soldiers or civilians who will operate them, and the necessary bunkers, sandbags, and weapons. There should be basic components, standarized in type and in technical characteristics, and completely compatible with the mobile communications equipment of the combat and area support signal units, capable of being put together in a building-block fashion.

For example, a modularized site of a certain capacity, say 60 channels, could be expanded to 100 or to 1,000 channels. It should be capable of being expanded further to include automated message and data traffic communications centers, local or long-distance automatic telephone exchanges—all from basic building blocks. All the equipment—the housing, the air conditioning, the power —must be of a fixed variety that can last in place for as long as five years without major overhaul. And everything must be so designed that the modules can be lifted to the sites by means of medium or heavy helicopters. There should be no need to build expensive access roads to mountaintops for the purpose of site construction.

Modules must be completely planned and engineered so that, even if they are not in the military inventory, their production can start as soon as approval is obtained. Production and procurement should be going on concurrently with the preparation of the sites in the area where they are required. To my mind, we can design such a building-block system within the next few years, and have the system reasonably available without going into production until it is actually needed. Basic ordering agreements could be made with the vendors, the radio equipment firm, the multiplex equipment firm, the air-conditioning firm, the tower unit firm, the building firm, and the power firm. If the modular system is too complex for the Army to install, then contracts must be let to firms capable of installing the complete package. On the matter of acquiring modularized systems, it is important to deliver equipment early to the Army service schools in the United States and to the war zone so that soldiers can train on the actual equipment to be used.

All the various transmission means, be they tropospheric scatter, microwave, satellite, cable, laser, or infra red, should be considered by the planners of the future when determinations are being made as to what best fits the military needs in a given situation. In Southeast Asia the undersea cable systems have provided some of the most reliable high quality communications within and to that area. The use of undersea cable connecting points along the coast of Vietnam was a significant innovation, and the opinion of some that the cables were not important because of the number of tropospheric scatter and microwave systems programmed at the same time was completely in error. Undersea cable has proved relatively inexpensive to maintain and is fairly simple to operate, even though it has a tremendously high initial cost. Within Vietnam, it provided backup to the remainder of the system and supplied very important dual routing for critical circuits. It is beyond question that military communications systems require diverse paths in order to provide the over-all reliability needed on the modern battlefield. The undersea cable served this purpose in Vietnam.

Requirements for the modular system would be based on the plans of the Department of Defense, the Joint Chiefs of Staff, and the military departments. And determining the needs—how much in the way of communications, how many circuits—can be very difficult. As General Abrams once said while talking to our combat signalmen in Vietnam: "You fellows belong to something that is almost a bottomless pit. No matter how big you make the system, there are more people going to want to talk over it and more people going to want to send things over it . . . ."

General Terry, who commanded and organized the 1st Signal Brigade during the big buildup years of 1966–1967, later had a study made called "Communications in Southeast Asia," for the purpose of finding out how requirements for future theaters might be determined. This valuable piece of work, in which many people co-operated, has fairly well documented the requirements of Vietnam at that time and is the first serious study of this type ever attempted during wartime. Although the study did not come up with all the answers, it should serve as a valuable tool for our planners, assisting them to develop requirements based on contingency plans. However, the entire area of communications requirements forecasting certainly needs more study in the next decade so that the Army, in any future war, can determine all of its communications requirements rapidly in order to assure equitable consideration by all levels during the decision process.

In summary, I believe the "Modular System," the Basic Ordering Agreement, and early detailed planning are the ingredients for the timely provision of a single integrated telecommunications system in a war zone in the future.

Automation of the Telephone System

The extensive use of dial telephone exchanges, eventually tied together with automated tandem switches providing direct distance dialing throughout Vietnam and Thailand, has been a significant development during the conflict in Vietnam. The manually operated telephone system, which we used and improved over a number of years, aside from being costly in the number of operators required, simply could not provide the needed services. One can imagine how expensive and how poor the service would be in the United States if our commercial telephone system was not highly automated. Because of the original poor manual service in Vietnam, 85 percent of the total voice channels were tied up as sole-use circuits, passing the most critical traffic, but unavailable for general use.

As one means of improving the telephone service when it was a manual system, the U.S. Military Assistance Command, Vietnam, had allowed only 30 percent of the thousands of telephone subscribers in the country to have direct access to the long-distance network. With the advent of direct distance dialing and the significant increase in long-distance calls made, we found that in order to provide the needed service a further reduction to 20 percent of the subscribers was necessary—a reduction that may seem to contradict the benefits of long-distance dialing. We were never able to perform adequate traffic analysis when the manual telephone system was being used; however, with the automatic long-distance telephone equipment, traffic loads could be accurately forecast. I am convinced that our experience in Vietnam proves that the number could be reduced to 15 percent of the subscribers and still not deny long-distance calls to any important customers. I also believe that the allocation of long-distance users by a predetermined percentage is the only means of providing the needed service throughout a theater at a reasonable cost in equipment and manpower. This percentage must be made a matter of policy at the Joint Chiefs of Staff level so that the communications planners can determine the size of the long-lines system in any future theater of operations.

The dial telephone exchanges and the long-distance automatic switches of the future, as I indicated before, should be modularized and installed as a part of the over-all integrated system. And they must be reasonably mobile, as were the 600-line van-mounted dial exchanges which the Army used in Vietnam. These mobile exchanges were employed in a number of different locations in Vietnam and were very important in crucial periods after the mid-1960s in providing a flexible dial telephone capability as needs shifted in Vietnam from one combat area to another.

Besides the demonstrated need for automatic telephone switching in the large camps and base areas, where this equipment was used in Vietnam, there is also a need for the combat telephone systems to be automated in the future. Manual telephone switchboards, now so prevalent at the division, brigade, and battalion command posts, cannot provide the speed of service required by our highly mobile fighting men. Besides providing automatic local telephone service, the combat communications systems, particularly at the corps and field army level, should be able to provide direct distance dialing. Automation of the mobile telephone switching systems is a must for the immediate future.

Communications Security

The vital matter of securing our communications against enemy interception and intelligence has been discussed, particularly with reference to the technically difficult area of scrambling telephone or voice traffic, especially the voice communications of the combat battalions and company-size units. Studies have shown the absolute necessity for communications security, whether the information is passed by message or voice. We know that the enemy listens in because we have captured some of his listening devices.

Voice security equipment has been available for some time in fixed communications installations at major headquarters and bases in the form of the Automatic Secure Voice Communications System. Secure voice gear is now available also for mobile radios. These first fixed systems were welcomed and used by higher headquarters. But it took a great deal of persuasion and training to get mobile combat users to employ voice security to the utmost with their field radios. We found that the most persuasive, effective way to insure its use was to provide proof that a given enemy action—an ambush of one of our patrols, for example—was the result of the enemy's intercepting our radio talk.

Good training in voice security—awareness of its necessity and a compulsion to use it—is the key. The training of officers and soldiers in the use of voice security needs command emphasis; it needs the assistance and insistence of commanders and other senior officers. I would say the only excuse for voice communications in the clear, that is, not secured or scrambled, is its use on an occasion when the information being passed is extremely current, say within ten minutes of action as in emergency situations. Anything more than this is unacceptable if we are to achieve success in any future battle.

We must be careful to develop and design security equipment that is completely compatible with the radios or other communications equipment and systems being used by our Army in the field. This was not the case in all instances in Vietnam. For example, the man-packed combat voice radios, used so extensively by almost all units in Vietnam, needed major modification before they could be used with our new man-packed voice security equipment. In the future we must guard against this by closer co-ordination and direction of our developmental programs to insure that all of the elements that make up a system are compatible.

Communications security devices, along with such practices as changing radio frequencies and call words, must be extensively employed in the future. They must be used for all combat orders, and all multichannel links must be completely secured. We could do a great deal, I am sure, to increase the security of our voice traffic and to improve the quality of transmission by following fixed-station standards. Whether in fixed or mobile applications, we must learn to use the security equipment we have, improving it technically and procedurally, improving also administrative matters and regulations relating to its use. All this will take practice and time, but it can and must be done to deny the enemy any knowledge of our plans and our commands.

Precedence and Classification of Messages

Two related matters in message traffic are security classification —Confidential, Secret, and Top Secret— and precedence, such as stamping a message "Immediate" or "Priority" if it is to be handled ahead of others. Such a message, if over one page long and if it includes a long list of information addressees—those addressees who must know the message content but do not need to take action or respond—causes problems and delays. In 1970 we were handling about 100,000 messages a day, of which about 60 percent had both action and information addressees. These could have been handled much more efficiently if the "Immediate" or "Flash" precedence applied only to those addressees who needed to take action and not to the copies which were for information only. The information copies could have been sent later by the communications center, during slack periods. Establishing such procedures is a must if we are to be "cost effective." These procedures could be further enhanced by both mobile and fixed automated message systems for terminal operation, such as the automated communications and message processing system activated in the Pacific near the end of the period covered by this study.

The same is true of much classified traffic initially stamped "Secret" and "Top Secret." If the traffic bore a notation to declassify at the end of one year, or two, this would be a great help. Again, it is in the matter of the information addressee messages that the overclassification becomes a problem—extremely lengthy messages require a teletypewriter tape to be reproduced, which amounts to typing the whole message over a second time. This happens at both the transmitting and the receiving end. In short it would be significantly helpful to reduce the size of messages, reduce the precedence, or at least reduce high precedence from information copies, and shorten significantly the effective periods of classification.

Physical Security at the Sites

Another kind of security, much more open and obvious than communications security, increasingly concerned the Army Signal Corps in Vietnam—physical security, the defense of our many sites. Defense measures were essential, as on some distant mountaintop sites, from the start of our operations in Vietnam in the 1950s. And security measures became necessary at more sites in 1969 and 1970, when troop units formerly based in the area around the signal installations left as a result of the redeployment of U.S. forces.

Our communications sites in Southeast Asia totaled from time to time between 250 and 300, and by no means were they all located in military compounds. Instead, these sites were often remote. Our combat signalmen provided for their own defense and at several sites fought off enemy attacks.

Obviously, the average signalman can be trained to serve well in site defense. He can be trained as an infantryman, both to defend his site and to patrol in depth around it. To this extent he needs to be a soldier first, and a soldier-technician second. But there is need for day-to-day use of artillery support in defense of our sites, for mortar and machine gun support, and for direct air support. There is need as well for security companies, whether U.S. troops or local nationals, trained as infantry. These troops are needed at the isolated signal site, whether run by a signal brigade,

TANK AND ANTENNA DISH—*Signal soldier-artist's conception of strong tie between Infantry, Armor, Artillery, and Signalman.*

division, corps, or field army, so that an integrated defense can be organized and maintained effectively.

The ground requirement was clearly apparent in Vietnam. While air defense, both active and passive, was not necessary in Vietnam, it probably will be required in the future. The active measures are obviously the ultimate responsibility of the U.S. Army's Air Defense Artillery; yet the communications planners must assure that, just as the engineer is notified for power requirements, the air defense artilleryman is made aware of all existing and planned communications sites when he is establishing his integrated air defense system. Passive air defense protection is equally essential. Methods must be developed to conceal and even cover our fixed communications sites. We cannot afford to take the chance in the future of building million dollar communications sites that can be "seen" visually and electronically by an attacking aircraft at great distances. The Army must investigate the areas of antenna and structure designs to be more in line with the principles of concealment. Thought must be given to "dummy" sites, again both visual and electronic, to protect against missiles as well as piloted aircraft.

A final note regarding security of our communications sites of the future is that the precedent established in Vietnam of providing the people of the country with circuits on our communications systems must be continued. The armed forces and government of the host country must be encouraged to use and share our communications systems, since the local populace has been and will undoubtedly continue to be a vital factor in the defense of our fixed communications facilities.

The Audio-Visual Mission

Photographic responsiblity in the Army has traditionally been assigned to the Signal Corps. This responsibility has expanded over the years to include far more than merely providing the photographers and photographic support. Today called the audio-visual mission, the responsibility encompasses not only the Army's pictorial services but the photographic history of the U.S. Army, and the operation and maintenance of a vast number of film projectors, magnetic tape recorders, and other audio and visual aids used extensively in command briefings and presentations. The Army Signal Corps today uses the most modern and advanced film laboratory equipment available in satisfying the Army's worldwide requirement for film and photographic services.

This audio-visual responsibility has not been emphasized in the past with the same fervor as have the Army's other communications services. In Vietnam it lagged, for example, in the 1st Signal Brigade until more pressing communications priorities and problems could be met. It was not until mid-1967 that the photographic effort was strengthened with the equipment and men of the 221st Signal Company.

The 221st Signal Company was provided with "off-the-shelf," commercial photographic equipment when it went to Vietnam because the Army's standard line of photographic equipment was not capable of doing the job in Vietnam. This one-of-a-kind signal unit created problems for the Army school system. The U.S. Army Signal School was fully capable of providing excellent and complete training in the audio-visual skills using standard equipment, but it could not teach maintenance and operation of the commercially purchased cameras, automated laboratory processing equipment, or projectors. These skills were taught in Vietnam by the expedient of on-the-job training. It was, of course, not feasible for the Army to reorganize its entire training program in order to satisfy the needs of one specialized unit equipped with commercial items, but attention must be given to training signalmen in the use of the most modern equipment in order to have them available for the Army's Audio-Visual Program in war zones.

In the future, efforts must be made to establish early a completely equipped and trained audio-visual support base in the combat zone. Even the full strength of the 221st Signal Company did not provide all the audio-visual support the Army needed in Vietnam. We need to be able to make pictures in both color and black and white and we need more magnetic tape voice equipment for our movies. We should make greater use of film strip projectors and audio-visual devices for briefings at both combat and the highest levels. We should be able to produce a motion picture within at least a week in the theater of operations. Further, the over-all direction of photographic collection must be improved, particularly the effort to record historical events on film. Our officers and managers of the Audio-Visual Program must have a sense for the history that is being made.

Personnel and Training

All of the most modern and sophisticated equipment available will not insure workable communications unless the commander has an adequate number of trained communicators. This portion of my conclusions will deal with the soldier-communicator.

It is essential that significant efforts be made by all Signal Corps officers to acquire an intimate knowledge of the Army's personnel acquisition system, its personnel authorization system, and other essential elements of personnel management. With this preparation, the career Signal Corps officer at any level of command will be better able to cope with the intricacies of the Army's personnel system and insure that the approved authorizations are in the hands of the signal unit in the war zone and that the authorized soldiers are in fact assigned and working.

In regard to the personnel system and signal units, it is most important that 100 percent of the men authorized be on the job. I am not referring to a select group of signal units, but to all signal units at all levels. Communications from top to bottom is a team effort, and this effort can succeed only if the signal soldier is available at all levels to provide the required communications. To attain 100 percent of authorized strength on the job, I believe that we must staff the signalmen in the combat zone at 110 percent of the authorized level. It has been my experience that in this war, as in World War II and Korea, an allowable overstrength is the only sure way of attaining the 100 percent assigned strength so essential to complete the job.

One of the significant personnel lessons the Army's Signal Corps learned in Vietnam was that it is extremely cumbersome and slow to attempt to transfer into a combat zone the personnel system used for the processing of authorization documents in a peacetime environment. The system I refer to is The Army Authorization Documents System, known as TAADS in Army jargon. From late 1968 to mid-1969 the 1st Signal Brigade and divisional units submitted new proposed authorization documents through regular channels to the Department of the Army. It took about a year and a half for these documents to be approved, and meanwhile the war continued with great intensity. I feel we must speed up the process for authorization approval to less than three months. Immediate steps need to be taken to reduce document-processing time at intermediate headquarters and at the Department of the Army. Consideration should be given to standardized automated programs that can be used at all command echlelons for annotating and processing authorization document updates. The automated outputs could be accompanied by written justification for changes, that is by additions or deletions to current authorizations.

After spending almost twenty months to complete a major reorganization cycle necessitated by changing operations in a war, I feel that decentralization to the heads of major commands in the Army of the power to approve changes within their personnel and equipment levels is a requirement, a must, if the Army's authorization system is to survive during a war.

While still on the subject of personnel, I would like to discuss Signal Corps officers as professional communicators assigned to all organizations down to all types of maneuver battalions. It was proved to all the division commanders, corps commanders, and theater commanders that it was a necessity to have a professionally trained Signal Corps officer assigned to each battalion, group, and brigade of the Army's combat arms. It was necessary in order to create a vertical chain of communications officers from the bottom to the top—officers whose professional training and interests had dedicated them to the accomplishment of the communications-electronics mission. Each of these officers was able to translate his commander's needs into actual working communications. Through these officers, the commander was made aware of the capabilities, the limitations, and the peculiarities of his own communications system. The Army training program, like the Communications Officers Course at Fort Sill, Oklahoma, should be used extensively to produce such trained Signal Corps officers for combat battalions; and the officers who attend the course should be assigned immediately to combat battalions in order that the Army can take full advantage of their capabilities.

I have strong convictions on the kind of training base we should have in the United States and on the matter of maintaining a pool of trained signalmen with the necessary skills to meet contingencies such as the Vietnam War. Early in the 1960s, the Army had decided that the use of cable was dying out, if not already dead. Instead, radio was the word. We in the Signal Corps "thought radio" from the infantry squad level up to the theater level. As a result, the specialty of cable-splicer was deleted from the Army's schooling program.

The fallacy of this decision became apparent when we were installing the high quality, fixed wideband system in Southeast Asia. We found we did not have the trained soldiers available to splice in the final few feet of cable, for example, from the electronic equipment building of a big fixed tropospheric scatter terminal to a dial telephone exchange a half-mile away. A pool of cable-splicers, trained at our own U.S. Army schools with the same equipment the soldier will use in the field rather than with makeshift equipment and materials, is necessary if the Army ever expects to build again as elaborate a communications system as that installed in Vietnam.

I do not isolate cable-splicing as the one critical skill required. I consider essential the skills of the technical controllers, microwave and tropospheric scatter operators, communications chiefs, radio teletypewriter operators, cryptographic and secure voice equipment repairmen, dial exchange and automatic switch operators and maintenance personnel, and switchboard operators. Army signalmen with these skills are so essential that they should be part of a trained pool, available when needed. Ideally these soldiers should work in their specialties throughout their careers. But if this is not always possible, then we should at least know where the trained communicators are and be able to deploy them when the situation dictates. And there are needs for these trained soldiers within the United States at the communications facilities the Army is allowed to operate within the franchised area of U.S. common carriers.

The critical skills mentioned above do not of course extend across the complete spectrum of skills required for Army communications. Communications is a team effort, as I said before, and without the trained bread-and-butter signalmen, without the combat and fixed-type communications skills, the over-all job cannot be done.

In the matter of the Army's training centers in the United States, I believe these centers must receive new equipment that is to be introduced into the combat theater at about the same time as the Army's new equipment introductory teams receive it. For one reason or another this did not take place in the instance of Vietnam. The mistake should not be repeated. The prototype equipment must go to the signal schools or other electronic training centers. Military instructors should be with the manufacturer when the manufacturer's plans and equipment are being developed. If this procedure is not followed, major problems will arise. Repeatedly during the Vietnam War, new major equipment was introduced into the war zone and we had to train ourselves to operate and maintain it. The training base in the United States was operating months behind in new procedures and new equipment. Our solution, of course, was to establish a signal school, the 1st Signal Brigade's U.S. Army Training Facility.

This school was not unprecedented; such schools had existed during World War II. Training schools should be established in all overseas theaters to teach refresher courses for soldiers previously trained in the United States. The average signal soldier spends from two to nine months learning his specialty, then usually receives a month's leave before departing for his initial assignment. If he is assigned to an active war zone, the signal soldier needs a review of his specialty, just as the infantryman needs and gets a review of his trade before he is subjected to combat.

The 1st Brigade's training school in Vietnam was staffed by officers and men assigned to the brigade. Though the quality of instruction presented was continually outstanding, the short 12-month tour of the instructors posed a problem. A far more appropriate arrangement in the future would be to staff the school with civilian instructors under contract. The contractor would be responsible for school operation and instruction as long as the need existed and signal units would not have to draw from their own assets to man the school. Consideration should also be given to establishing the contract on a contingency basis so that valuable time will not be wasted while the contractor trains his own staff of instructors.

The preceding observations are not meant to detract from the tremendous job which the Army's school system in the United States—the best in the world—did in preparing the soldier to be a communicator in Vietnam; I was one of its "Commanders and Commandants" and intimately knew the entire training system.

Rather, I offer my observations in the hope of easing the burden of future communicators.

Supply and Maintenance

When the Army organized the U.S. Army Materiel Command some years ago and, in turn, its varied commodity-oriented subordinate commands, one of the key decisions was to place field representatives from these "commodity" commands with the Army's major overseas commands. I believe this was a correct move for all the elements of the Materiel Command, but in this instance I will restrict myself to the communications-electronics sphere and will discuss only the U.S. Army Electronics Command. I consider it very important that the Electronics Command, dynamically commanded by Major General William B. Latta during this period, be represented in any future combat theater, and, further, that it be closely aligned in every way, from the research laboratory to the field representative, with the communications-electronics staffs at the various commands, to include the combat unit level. To support communications-electronics maintenance operations, this commodity command must, at the very minimum, be represented in the field maintenance facilities at the logistics and signal commands in all theaters. These representatives may be Department of the Army civilian employees, technicians from the civilian company that made the equipment, or men hired by contract. The essential point is that Electronics Command representatives must be closely aligned with the various communications-electronics staff divisions and signal commands. It is entirely possible that further inquiry into this matter will reveal a firm requirement for Electronics Command liaison to reach down to and include the Army's combat brigades. As the communications for a division become more sophisticated I can foresee a real need for technical representation at that level and below.

It will not be enough merely to place technical representatives all over the world and advise the communicator in the field that an "area representative" is available for technical advice. The representatives in the field must physically be with the operating units, and the organization must be such that the field representative is in continuous communication with the laboratories and headquarters in the United States. Without this intimate interrelationship, it would have been impossible for us to do our communications job in Vietnam, and such an interrelationship will be more and more important in the future.

Earlier, I went to some length to present the evolution of the 1st Signal Brigade's area maintenance and supply facilities and the problems of trying to maintain and stock repair parts for unique, commercially procured communications equipment through the use of the Army's common supply system. I did this because I consider the matter to be one of our most important communications lessons from this war. That is, the general supply system, which processed and delivered millions of gallons of oil and gasoline and millions of tons of "beans and bullets" to Vietnam, is just not geared to satisfying a request for one small transistorized module, made only by XYZ Electronics Corporation, which is needed to put a key million dollar network back in operation. The Army's general supply system rightfully deals in volume and frequency of requests, whereas the fixed-plant communications system in Vietnam did not need frequent or large quantity resupply; as a result the computers in the supply system did not recognize infrequent demands as valid.

The instances of difficulties in obtaining unique communications-electronics items through the general supply system were many. The following example illustrates the rigidity of our general supply system, and while the matter did not seriously deter our efforts, it certainly was aggravating. The 1st Signal Brigade and the combat signal units installed hundreds of miles of multi-pair cable on U.S. bases during the war. They used a massive amount of cable-splicing and sealing material. As I recall, the cable-splicing material, which was used by only a limited number of signal units in Vietnam, was categorized in the Federal Stock Number System as an item under "Office Stationery." If the suppliers had been familiar enough with our classification system to look under "Office Stationery" for splicing and sealing material, we could have avoided the incongruous situation that resulted. For it was determined that the Army in Vietnam was ordering far too much office stationery, and therefore it was directed that requests in this category would not be honored unless they were personally signed by an officer of senior rank. For some time, try as we might, we could not get one item of cable-splicing material unless the request forms were personally signed by senior personnel. The problem was solved by setting up a special direct supply organization for cable material in the brigade, which was the only major user— a solution that must be credited to Lieutenant General Joseph M. Heiser, Jr., at the time the aggressive and able commander of logistics in Vietnam.

Our answer to the problems of maintenance and of obtaining

GENERAL RIENZI TALKS TO HELICOPTER CREW MEMBER IN THE MEKONG DELTA

repair items for the unique, fixed-station communications equipment was the establishment of the Area Supply and Maintenance Facilities within the Army's general supply system, and I believe that without them the relatively low density, yet high level, fixed communications installations would not have continued to operate in the highly effective manner so necessary for immediate command control.

Aviation

I am convinced that aircraft must be organic to every signal battalion in the Army, just as it is organic to many comparable organizations in the Army. At the height of the Vietnamese conflict, the 1st Signal Brigade was authorized 45 aircraft: 9 twin-engine, turbo-prop, fixed-wing aircraft; 12 light observation helicopters; and 24 utility helicopters. These aircraft were listed as organic on the authorization tables of each signal battalion in the brigade;

CONCLUSIONS AND LESSONS LEARNED

however, we pooled the aircraft in three provisional aviation units. One was based at Bearcat, near Long Binh, to support the 2d Signal Group in III and IV Corps Tactical Zones; the second in Nha Trang supported the 21st Signal Group in II Corps Tactical Zone; the third supported the 12th Signal Group, which was originally at Phu Bai and later at Da Nang in I Corps Tactical Zone. We learned that by pooling the aircraft we could accomplish by ourselves one-third of the maintenance that otherwise would have had to be done by aviation general support maintenance personnel. Without this organic airborne transportation, we could not possibly have supplied some 300 separate signal sites twenty-four hours a day, on the shortest notice.

Monetary Requirements

Establishing and operating a modern communications system for the U.S. Army today is a massively expensive proposition. In order to assure that the money being spent on communications was spent properly and that the civilian contracts were administered correctly, I feel it was important that we had comptroller staffs at both U.S. Army, Vietnam, and the 1st Signal Brigade, as well as completely up the command lines to Department of the Army and U.S. Army Strategic Communications Command Headquarters at Fort Huachuca, Arizona. I would even go so far as to recommend that comptroller positions be established even at the signal group level so that the money required to provide communications-electronics can be watched in some way and audited, regardless of whether the support is provided by the military or by civilian contract. The comptroller function should be part and parcel of any command function in future communication operations since the commander needs the comptroller in order to manage effectively the assets of his command and provide an auditable trail in short-tour war areas.

My final point in regard to money is that I take issue with the dollar limitation on the funding of communications projects. In mid-1969 the Secretary of Defense placed a $50,000 ceiling on communications projects that could be approved by the theater commander. Any project whose costs exceed that amount of money must receive approval from the Defense Department. That the process can take a long time is witnessed by the many months that passed before the Integrated Wideband Communications System project was approved. I feel certain that during war this $50,000 threshold is far too low. A more realistic ceiling would be

$1,000,000 to $2,000,000 for the theater Army commander or any major U.S. Army commander to approve. This higher threshold would allow flexibility in the management and operation of a billion dollar communications-electronics plant such as the Army possessed in Vietnam.

Vietnamization

Finally, we come to a matter of paramount importance and a major objective of the United States in recent months in Vietnam —the Vietnamization of communications. Training the Vietnamese to take over the systems we have built in their country has, of course, been a matter of deep concern to all of us. Since it began in the mid-1960s the "Buddies Together" program paired together officers and men of both the U.S. and South Vietnamese Armies —battalion commanders and executive officers, company commanders, officers and men at every level—in order to improve the communications know-how of our Vietnamese allies. Throughout the last half of the 1960s this program bore good fruit, notably in turnover to the Vietnamese of the Dong Tam Integrated Communications System site when the 9th Infantry Division departed in early 1970. It bore fruit also in the achievements of the Vietnamese divisions that replaced U.S. divisions.

The entire program now becomes extremely important during our phase-out from Vietnam, as the systems which the Vietnamese can use are turned over to them. These communications are first to be operated by U.S. civilian contractors. Later, they will be turned over to the Vietnamese who have been trained in the Vietnam signal school, or in the new U.S. contractor-operated Signal Training Facility, both at Vung Tau. The contract school also will be turned over to the Vietnamese to help them build a viable communications system for the future.

Eventually, a Single Integrated Telecommunications System— nicknamed SITS—will be welded together, serving the Republic of Vietnam armed forces, and serving civilians through an autonomous agency at the top level of the South Vietnamese Government. The foundations for all this are now in being, and the work continues to progress under the 1st Signal Brigade commander in Southeast Asia. If we go on at the current pace, the Vietnamese should soon have a communications system adequate for the nation's needs. We must press ahead energetically in the training program in communications-electronics in order to enable the South Vietnamese to unite their country.

The Great American Soldier

"Man is the measure of all things" has been a concise statement of a fundamental fact of life since the days of ancient Greece. And unquestionably the degree to which Army communications-electronics in Vietnam surpassed all military signaling ever known until now reflects precisely the degree to which the American military signalmen of this war surpassed their predecessors.

It has been my experience, as it was the universal experience of my predecessors in the divisional and field force signal battalions and in the 1st Signal Brigade, that the quality and performance of our enlisted men and officers in combat in Vietnam have notably excelled the levels attained in our previous conflicts. The number of men who failed to "measure up" has been far less; the levels of bravery, morale, dedication, intelligent and aggressive application, technical aptitude, and leadership have been very noticeably higher.

Many a youthful second lieutenant or sergeant found himself in complete command of an isolated signal site, fully responsible for a small self-contained city of signalmen, support troops, security guards, and often civilian contract personnel. Almost without exception the young officers met the challenge. One of them, Second Lieutenant Roberto Rivera, so impressed General Abrams when he and his party landed in their helicopter on a brigade site in Thailand near the Laotian border that General Abrams promoted the young Signal Corps officer to first lieutenant on the spot.

For whatever reason, whether because of the American heritage, family and school background, military training, or the opportunities and challenges encountered in Army communications in Vietnam, I found the overwhelming majority of our soldiers to be dedicated, purposeful, knowledgeable, and brave. Not only is our combat signalman intelligent, eager, and trainable in any skill, but he is also a man of great feeling and empathy in his relations with his own fellow soldiers, with his counterpart in the Vietnamese Army—the Vietnamese signalman—and with the Vietnamese people.

Our signalman may be little known or seldom recognized, but day in and day out, night in and night out, he keeps the circuits humming, be they mobile or fixed. He keeps communications in and operating around the clock, however adverse the conditions of weather or combat. He improvises ways and means when trouble develops. He learns quickly the idiosyncrasies of the equipment, whether new or old, whether relatively simple or amazingly complex, often to an extent beyond the imagination of those skilled in the art of electronics. In Vietnam he has defended his sites and truly achieved the goal of "Keep the Shooters Talking."

Furthermore, our signalman can fight off the enemy. He knows his weapons and the security and combat skills of the infantryman, for he must build bunkers around his exposed equipment, lay out and man perimeter defenses, and fight—as he did notably in *Tet,* when the casualties of the 1st Signal Brigade mounted into the hundreds and the combat death toll was twenty-two. There is, for example, the case of Private, First Class, Thomas M. Torma, a Silver Star winner of the 86th Signal Battalion, who was badly wounded in an attack on the signal relay site atop Black Virgin Mountain—*Nui Ba Den*—near Tay Ninh, on the night of 13 May 1968. A satchel charge blasted his weapon from his hands, but he met an oncoming enemy and killed him with his bare hands.

In conclusion, I cannot overemphasize my profound regard for the greatness of our officers and men as I saw and worked with them in Vietnam: the enlisted men, the lieutenants and the captains, and the senior leaders, who learned from our military training system and who further trained themselves on the job for whatever tasks and whatever team efforts were required to build and operate the gigantic communications-electronics network in Vietnam while the U.S. Army was fighting a war.

> "May it be said well done.
> Be thou at peace."

Index

Abrams, General Creighton W.: 47, 58, 104, 150, 157, 173

Advisers, U.S.: 5–6, 13, 17, 25, 49, 63–64, 68, 76, 108, 112, 150, 152

Agency for International Development: 6, 8, 152

Air bases, defense of: 22

Air bombardment: 142

Air conditioners: 109

Air Force, Seventh: 25. *See also* United States Air Force.

Air support. *See* Tactical air support.

Airborne Brigade, 173d: 24, 31, 55, 65, 68, 121

Airborne radio systems: 34, 97, 99, 122–25

Aircraft. *See also* Helicopters.
  B–52: 35
  Caribou: 34, 124
  deployed to Vietnam: 5
  future defense against: 162
  Otter: 124
  in signal units: 170–71
  Ute: 124

Airlifts: 24, 33, 81–82, 107

Airmobile concept, test and application: 34–35

Airmobile divisions: 63
  1st Cavalry: 31–35, 55, 104, 113, 123–24, 148
  101st Airborne: 95, 104, 113, 134

Airports, operations at: 81

Ambushes, enemy: 82–84, 109, 121

Amphibious operations: 117–20

An Khe: 32–33, 68, 82, 125

Antenna systems: 9–10, 28, 119–20, 162

Area Supply and Maintenance Facilities: 170

Area system concept: 48–52, 59. *See also* Army Area Communications System; Corps Area Communications System.

Armored Cavalry Regiment, 11th: 148–50

Army, Department of the: 13, 26, 39, 41, 47–48, 58, 79, 123–24, 128, 137–38, 140, 147, 165, 171

Army Area Communications System: 48

Army Communications Agency: 21

Army Communications Operations Center: 75

Army Communications Systems, Vietnam: 74

Army Regional Communications Group: 52–53

Army Signal Command, Vietnam: 41, 47

Army Signal Engineering Agency: 21

Army Signal Supply Point: 10

Army Training Facility: 98, 137, 145, 167

Artillery units: 60, 117, 120, 162

Assistant Secretary of Defense: 79

Audio-visual support. *See* Photography.

Australia: 152

Automatic Digital Network: 89, 91–92, 132–35, 137

Automatic Secure Voice Communications System: 92–93, 120–24, 150, 159–60

Automatic telephone systems: 38–40, 73–74, 88–89, 92, 99, 135, 143, 145, 147–48, 158–59

Automatic Voice Network: 135

Ba Queo: 15, 94

BACK PORCH system: 7–10, 19–21, 26–28, 76

Bamberg, Staff Sergeant Gerald H.: 84

Ban Me Thuot: 6, 11, 13, 104, 111

Bang Pla, Thailand: 6, 94, 135

Bangkok, Thailand: 16, 39, 53, 94, 140

Base camps: 49, 57, 59–60, 62–63, 154, 159

Bearcat: 171

Bell Telephone System: 76

Ben Het: 68

Ben Tre: 104

Benewah, USS: 118–20

Bien Hoa: 31, 37, 49, 111

Black Virgin Mountain: 111, 150, 174

Blackwell, Lieutenant Colonel Lotus B.: 10

Buddy System: 144, 172

Bulldozers, interference by: 51

White, Major Leo T.: 22

Wideband systems: 15. *See also* Integrated Communications System, Southeast Asia; Integrated Wideband Communications System.

Williamson, Brigadier General Ellis W.: 31

World War II experience: 41, 57, 121

YELLOWSTONE operation: 112

☆ U.S. GOVERNMENT PRINTING OFFICE: 1972 O—450–007

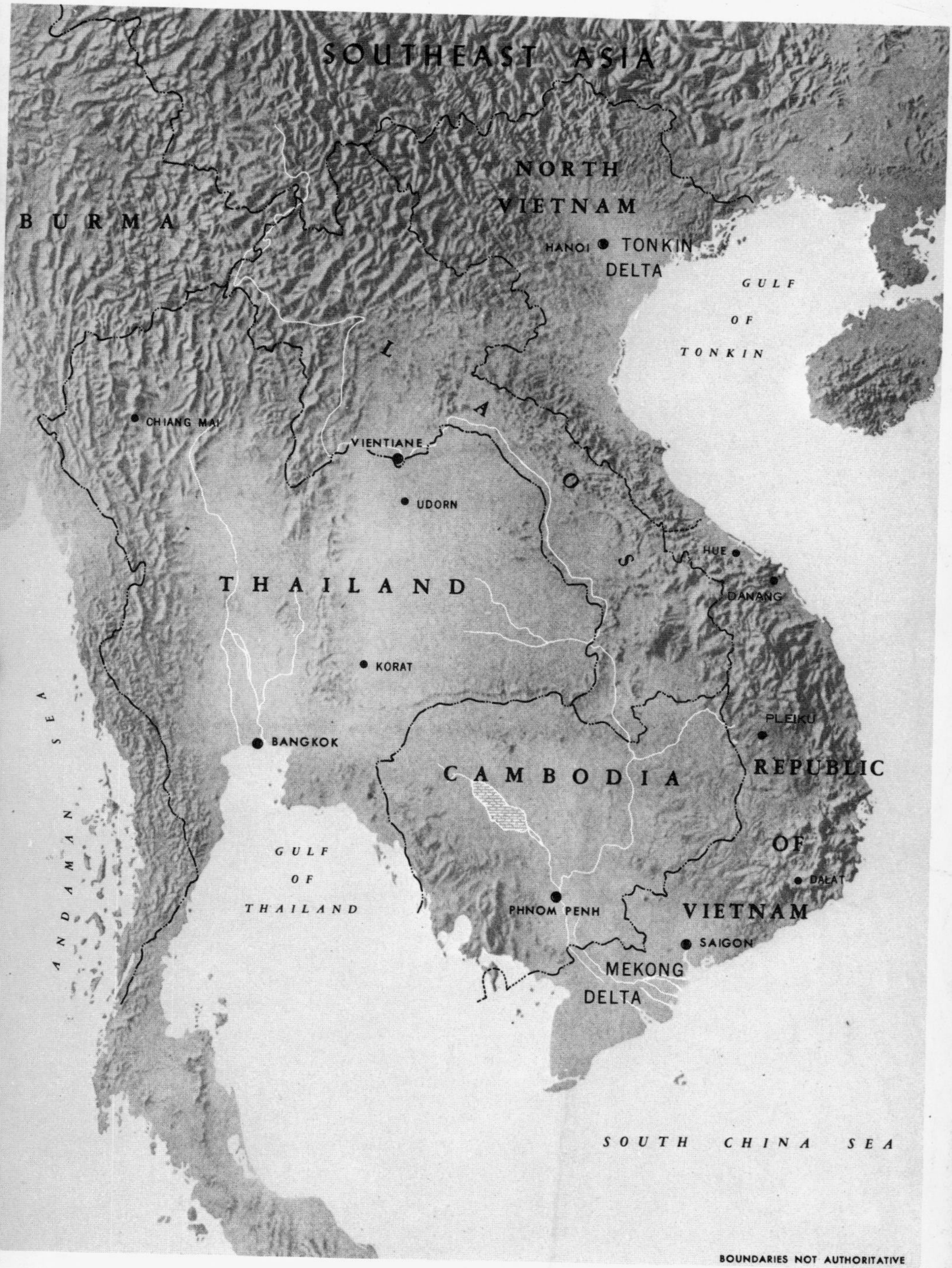

SOUTHEAST ASIA

BURMA

NORTH
VIETNAM

HANOI ● TONKIN
DELTA

GULF
OF
TONKIN

● CHIANG MAI

VIENTIANE
●

L A O S

● UDORN

THAILAND

HUE ●
DANANG ●

● KORAT

PLEIKU
●

CAMBODIA

REPUBLIC

OF

BANGKOK ●

GULF
OF
THAILAND

PHNOM PENH ●

VIETNAM

DALAT ●

SAIGON ●

MEKONG
DELTA

ANDAMAN SEA

SOUTH CHINA SEA

BOUNDARIES NOT AUTHORITATIVE